The Disciplined Imagination

An Approach to
the Reading of Fiction

Gerald E. Enscoe
Robert W. Russell

Franklin and Marshall College

The Disciplined Imagination

An Approach to the Reading of Fiction

ADDISON-WESLEY PUBLISHING COMPANY
Reading, Massachusetts · Menlo Park,
California · London · Don Mills, Ontario

Imagination applied to the whole world is vapid in comparison to imagination applied to a detail.

Wallace Stevens
Adagia

. . . nothing can be more obviously useful than learning to read and write and talk, but . . . a lot of people, especially young and inexperienced people, don't see why studying literature should be a necessary part of this. . . . Literature speaks the language of the imagination, and the study of literature is supposed to train and improve the imagination. But we use our imagination all the time: it comes into all our conversation and practical life: it even produces dreams when we're asleep. Consequently we have only the choice between a badly trained imagination and a well trained one.

Northrop Frey
The Educated Imagination

CONTENTS

PART ONE
THE NATURE OF FICTION

Introduction   1

PART TWO
STORIES AND QUESTIONS FOR
INTENSIVE ANALYSIS

Introduction   19

Ernest Hemingway	Cat in the Rain 20
Saki (H. H. Munro)	Sredni Vashtar 36
James Joyce	Araby 48
Nathaniel Hawthorne	Young Goodman Brown 63

PART THREE
SECTIONED STORIES

Introduction   94

John Galsworthy	The Japanese Quince 96
Stephen Crane	The Bride Comes to Yellow Sky 100
Sherwood Anderson	Seeds 110
Robert Penn Warren	The Life and Work of Professor Roy Millen 117
Ring Lardner	Anniversary 124
Rudyard Kipling	The Mark of the Beast 133

PART FOUR
STORIES FOR FURTHER STUDY

Introduction   143

Eudora Welty	A Visit of Charity 144

D. H. Lawrence   The Rocking-Horse Winner   149
Edgar Allan Poe   The Black Cat   161
William Carlos Williams The Use of Force   168
Ambrose Bierce   The Boarded Window   171
J. F. Powers   The Valiant Woman   175
Frank O'Connor   First Confession   182
William Faulkner   A Rose for Emily   189
Flannery O'Connor   A Good Man Is Hard to Find   196
Delmore Schwartz   In Dreams Begin Responsibilities   208

Reading good fiction ought to be almost as exciting and satisfying as living. It won't be, but nothing is. It hurts us more to prick our finger with a needle than to read about the princess who pricked hers. Art can't quite match the actual experience of physical pain or pleasure, but, on the other hand, it has some advantages.

The first is compression. In three or four hundred pages a writer can present the crucial events in the lives of his characters. Because we see how fictional characters react in critical situations, we can know more about them than about many of our friends. Our friends have the disadvantage, too, of being too close for us to get a full view of them; they also are inclined to change. A fictional character doesn't affect our judgment of him by buying us a milkshake or by snubbing us at a party. He is far enough away so that we get a good look at him, and he doesn't change in the same way that living people do. Upon rereading, we find that if he does change during the course of the story, he always does so at the same point and in the same way. Because the writer can compress time and give us more information about people who remain somewhat distant and stable, the reader enjoys that pleasure peculiar to humans of knowing and understanding other human beings. So, while the writer can't produce the actual experience, he can produce some things that in certain respects are better—a complete view of the lives of his characters and a fuller understanding of them.

Whether love scene or murder, the reader's experience is vicarious, but it is still an experience, and in some respects it may be more arresting, more meaningful than if it were first hand. In order for this to happen, both—book and reader—must be good. This may at first seem an odd notion because we hear so much more about good and bad books than we do about good and bad readers. The fact is that the quality of the reader is almost as important as the quality of the writer. Champagne and caviar are only alcohol and fish eggs to some savage, but they give exquisite pleasure to more refined palates. So the richness and power of a great story may mean nothing to an unsophisticated reader. In such a case, the loss isn't the writer's, but the reader's. The difference between a sophisticated and an unsophisticated reader is hard to define precisely, but two main differences are obvious. First, the sophisticated reader enjoys reading, and second, he

1

enjoys it because he enters imaginatively into what he is reading. It is this second point—the imaginative entrance into what he reads—that is the source of pleasure in the reading of fiction. Like any other ability, this capacity can be developed. It is to the development of the reader's power of imaginative entrance into fiction that this book is dedicated. If asked why we want to do this, our answer is simple. Helping others to richer enjoyment is to spread pleasure which, like love, grows with the sharing.

Every athlete and musician knows that quality performance rests on practice. This book is designed to exercise those faculties necessary to good reading. Like all exercises, the ones in these pages will sometimes seem trivial, annoying, and frustrating. We don't think they are, and if you give them the time and care they deserve, we think you will come to agree with us.

Most people read fiction faster than they are able to. To put it more obviously, recognizing words is not what we mean by reading; good fiction is not written simply to convey information. The writer chooses particular words, particular figures of speech because he wishes to create a particular impression, a special atmosphere within which the events he is relating take on special significance. To race through Camus, Joyce, or Hemingway merely to find out what happens is not to read those writers. In fact, one cannot really know what happens unless one reads with the care and sensitivity we are trying to encourage. The events of a plot take on color and significance only when we are familiar with the characters which they affect and the atmosphere within which they take place. If you've ever tried to summarize your favorite book for someone who hasn't read it, you know what we mean. It's an impossible task. The person who hasn't read the book has no feeling for the characters, so what happens to them is almost meaningless to him. A newspaper account of an automobile accident will probably mean very little if you do not know the people. If they are your closest friends, that same account could be devastating.

What this book seeks to do is to slow you up in your reading so that you can get the feel of the story, become acquainted with the characters, and have a sense of the context or atmosphere in which they move. The careful reading of a good piece of fiction should be a moving and dramatic experience, one which the reader should live through and which he should take pleasure in reliving.

The living or experiencing of a story is what we mean by entering it. This, after all, can be the only reason why we reread a book or a story, or go to see a play or a movie for a second or a third time. It isn't the plot that draws us back because we know how that turns out. It isn't the "how things turn out" that we actually care very much about. What we want to do is to go back and relive that unique dramatically patterned experience. We want to feel again the atmosphere and tensions of each scene and the mounting drama of that specific succession of scenes.

If you're skeptical about this, ask a football fan if he'll sell you his ticket for the big game on Saturday. Explain to him that instead of sitting on that hard seat in that screaming crowd—it may even snow—he can have a peaceful afternoon at home, maybe even get the car washed and catch up on some of those other jobs he's been meaning to do. He won't have to fight his way through the traffic jam. You'll do that for him. You'll go straight to the nearest phone and call him to let him know the final score.

He won't accept, and the reason he won't is that he wants to "see the game," by which he means that he wants to live each play. He wants to feel the excitement while the quarterback calls the signals on third down with four yards to go. He wants to feel that emptiness in his stomach, that terrible mixture of hope and fear when Bart Starr rolls out and sends the ball whirling thirty yards down field toward his left end who is furiously trying to outrace and outfake two defenders. Will he catch it? Will it be intercepted? Those moments — that's what he means by "seeing the game." The final score is distinctly secondary. The sophisticated sports fan would eagerly watch the filmed replay of a good game he has seen. He feels about a great game the same way that a sophisticated reader feels about a great book. The reader, though, has important advantages over the sports fan. There are a lot more great books than there are great games. Books are available everywhere, so there are abundant opportunities for imaginative entrance into many great experiences. When this entrance is made, the story matters because the reader himself cares about all that occurs. Disappointments and surprises are happening not to empty names, but to people whom he knows. The story becomes part of his personal experience. With *Grapes of Wrath* John Steinbeck succeeded in making millions of Americans feel what it was like to be an "Okie," and because they had suffered, though vicariously, public pressure was exerted to help these dispossessed people. When such a book becomes very popular, one usually hears of the success of the writer, but we are more concerned with the success of the reader—that is, the skills with which he imaginatively enters a piece of fiction.

In order to develop this skill, it is necessary to have some awareness of the basic elements that make up a piece of fiction and the way they operate. With such awareness we can consciously work to improve the quality of our experience with fiction, to become more successful readers.

Though no definition of fiction will be completely satisfactory, there are certain elements that we can isolate in every piece of fiction in order to think about them. By fiction we mean *a piece of writing which presents a direct appeal to the reader's imagination through a sequence of details which reveal particular characters in particular settings, acting and interacting with each other in relation to certain events and situations — all of which taken together in this particular combination conveys a vision of what human life is like.*

3

The key terms in the above definition are *Imagination, Sequence,* and *Vision.* Let's examine each of them in some detail.

Imagination and the Elements of Fiction

The writer of fiction, like a playwright, appeals to an audience, but the fiction writer's audience is the solitary reader. The playwright, on the other hand, writes not only for his audience but for actors and directors who are a part of the medium of drama. The actor's speech, costume, makeup, gestures, the stage scenery, the various props, and theatrical devices are all tools the playwright has at his disposal to achieve his effect. He appeals immediately and directly to the sense of sight and hearing, with living people acting out his tale. His is a public act performed, hopefully, before large crowds. The theatergoer's imagination is stimulated and his understanding of the playwright's vision is supported by other devices as well as by language.

The art of the novelist or story writer, on the other hand, is private. He has only the medium of the printed page through which to make his appeal to the sensibilities and imagination of his reader. His audience is a single, silent person sitting alone under a lamp in an easy chair in his livingroom, at the kitchen table with a cup of coffee growing cold beside him, or propped by pillows late at night in the stillness of a bedroom. Wherever the reader is, his only contact with the story comes through the silent, motionless sheet of printed paper before him. Whatever he makes of that page, he must make by himself without the corroborating chuckle or tense stillness of a theater, which shows him that others feel about this scene as he does. While the writer of fiction hopes to involve his reader as completely as the dramatist hopes to capture his audience, he has fewer tools to do it with. His success depends entirely upon his reader's sensitivity to the printed word.

Being sensitive to words means more than being familiar with their definitions. It means being capable and willing to respond imaginatively and emotionally to them and to what they suggest. It is automatic to feel tension and suspense when you see a door open quietly behind a character on a movie screen and a gun barrel slowly emerge. It is another thing to respond fully to a printed description of that scene. The writer must get the reader to *imagine* that situation, to recreate it in his mind's eye. Until the reader does that, he cannot respond emotionally. So the reader must work actively to create the *image* or scene. He must be producer, director, set designer, actor, and, on top of all this, the audience.

Thus the specific details, the words, which the writer chooses to describe and define the *characters,* the *setting,* the *action,* the particular *events,* and *situations* are all signals to the reader's imagination, the basic building materials of fiction out of which the reader must imaginatively construct the story.

Let's examine each of these elements the reader must use.

Character. Characters are the human personalities to whom things happen in fiction, and through whom meaning is given to fictitious events. Strictly speaking, characters do not exist *in* a work of fiction; they exist in the reader's mind. The writer of fiction utilizes several techniques in order to give the reader sufficient material out of which to construct the characters and bring them into existence.

The most obvious is physical description. Nothing in a work of fiction is accidental, and when the writer describes the appearance of his characters, the details are chosen so that the reader should imagine a particular person. Physical description is not an end in itself, but a means by which the personality of the character may also be imagined. And ultimately it is the personality we care most about.

5

Readers of A. A. Milne will remember that Pooh is neither slender nor agile. He is described as stout, and we must imagine him stumping through the forest with cheerful, simple-hearted honesty. But his stoutness has a bearing upon those endearing qualities. His shape is appropriate as a means of conveying the "human" qualities he possesses. If he were a nimble, surefooted bear, this would suggest an entirely different personality to the imagination and convey a different set of human qualities.

A particular character is further suggested in print, as in life, by what he says and by what he does. His dialogues with other characters, his thoughts, the kinds of things he is described as doing, are all details out of which the reader's imagination constructs a total picture. As readers we must keep asking, "What do the details of appearance, thought, feelings, and actions suggest to us about the nature of this person we are being encouraged to create?" But details of character do not exist in vacuums. They are combined with others suggesting particular places or settings, which in turn invite us to create particular atmospheres.

Setting. Setting is the atmosphere which the reader must imaginatively create from the details of the physical environment in which the characters are located. The first paragraph of James Joyce's "Araby" presents a good many physical details, but if you merely pointed them out, you would not have described the setting. The importance of these details lies in the aura, emotional climate, or dominant atmosphere which they suggest. The sense of oppression, loneliness, and immobility created from the details is the context within which the central character has his experience. Not to be aware of this is to lose much of the dramatic force of the story.

Setting is important because it is the emotional atmosphere or background within which or against which the characters act. Some characters in a story are unaware of their setting—for example, the husband in Hemingway's "Cat in the Rain." Others are acutely conscious of it—for example, Conradin in Munro's "Sredni Vashtar." The degree to which a character is conscious of his emotional environment tells us how sensitive he is. This is crucial information, because it tells us a great deal about the kind of person he is. Setting reveals character.

In summary, then, the reader should be sharply aware of the details of environment in order to create the appropriate atmosphere within which the characters move. Not to be aware of these may lead him to construct an atmosphere inappropriate to the actions and reactions of the characters, and such inappropriate constructions could lead him to misunderstand the story.

Action. Action is what the characters do. The details describing it are like stage directions for your imagination to work with in order to produce the particular action the writer has in mind. But there is more to it than this. Action has meaning and we must interpret as well as recreate it.

We usually judge people by their actions. Someone might suddenly seize you from behind and throw you to the ground, and someone else might rise to give you his seat in a crowded bus. These actions appear to tell us something about the character of the people performing them, but they don't. To understand those actions, we must also know something about the motives that prompted them. The person giving you his seat may actually be concerned about your comfort, or he may be hoping to pick your pocket as you brush past. The person who threw you down might intend to rob and beat you, or he might be trying to hurl you out of the path of a runaway car. Motive or intent, then, is so crucial an element that it is almost impossible to interpret actions without knowledge of the reasons that prompted the actor to perform them.

The writer of fiction usually surrounds the physical actions with significant details which help the reader to interpret the motives behind the action. He may describe what the character is thinking as well as what he is doing; in some cases he might describe for the reader things about the character that the character himself doesn't know.

If, for example, we were to accuse Conradin's cousin in "Sredni Vashtar" of enjoying her cruelty to the boy, she would be outraged. She would plead innocence, and she would think she was being completely honest, but we would know that while she would not be lying she would not be telling the truth simply because she did not know the truth about herself. The reader knows more about her motives than she does because the author described her actions with certain details revealing her motives. We know her better than she knows herself. We understand her actions.

Event. An event is that which happens in fiction. It may happen to the characters directly; it may happen to the setting within which the characters move; occasionally it happens miles away. But wherever it happens and whomever it happens to, it affects the characters in some way. It could be a storm, a war, an accident. In Hemingway's "Cat in the Rain," a cat wanders into the square during a rainstorm. This event produces a series of actions and reactions by the main characters. The event, meaningless in itself, is made meaningful because of the effect it has.

7

The details of the event, besides helping the reader to construct it in his own mind, usually suggest the relationship between the event and the characters. For example, the cat in Hemingway's story is alone, unloved, and pitiful; later we find a similarity between the cat's situation and that of the wife.

Situation. A situation is a set of problems or challenges which a character faces. They may be physical, psychological, or a combination of both. Writers of much popular fiction, stories of war, adventure, and rugged action, usually limit the situation to the physical—how to escape from hungry cannibals, how to capture an enemy outpost, how to track down a ferocious, man-eating tiger. But in most good fiction, as in our lives, the situation is almost never merely physical.

All of us have relationships with other people—mother, friend, brother, teacher, employer, neighbor—and they create part of our psychological situation. How we act depends upon our sense of these relationships. Characters in good fiction are placed in a particular situation, defined partly by physical details, partly by the details of their relationships with others, and partly by the details of their own feelings and emotions. *Conradin* feels his cousin to be a powerful enemy who enjoys making him suffer; *she* thinks him a nuisance who needs constant governing. Their feelings and thoughts about each other create the psychological situation within which each must act.

Actions and events can only be clearly understood when you, the reader, are fully aware of the situation. How should you react to an invitation that you would rather not accept? Would it be wise to risk giving offense, or would it be worse to accept and miss a better invitation? What is the best approach to an instructor who you think has been grading you unfairly? Before acting in either of these situations, you need to have a clear sense of your own feelings and a clear estimate of the other person's character. When you understand these things, you have a view of your situation. Whether it is actually the right or the wrong view will make a difference, but, right or wrong, you are aware of being in a situation, and you know what we mean by the term.

The writer of good fiction provides the details from which the good reader constructs the characters, the setting, the action, the events, and the situations. When your imagination is trained sufficiently well to focus upon details and create from them these important elements of fiction, you will have taken the first and most important step toward full participation in the art of reading fiction.

You need not be familiar with all the elements that contribute to the imaginative experience of fiction before you can read a story with pleasure, any more than a child needs to know the principles of grammar before he can speak. A child hears so much English that he gradually absorbs the fundamental speech patterns, though no one has consciously taught him. He like tales of Peter Rabbit and Winnie-the-Pooh long before he has ever heard of such things as character, action, setting, event, or situation. But just as it is a long way from monosyllabic communication to the accurate expression of a complex idea, so it is a long journey from Peter Rabbit to James Joyce, and some careful training can make that journey more swift and less difficult.

It should be helpful to think about these elements, for each is an aspect which, when explored, should lead the reader to experience more fully that patterned sequence of complex tensions which is the story. They should be regarded as ways into a story, not as ways through it. Focusing, for example, on details of setting makes us conscious of the medium in which the characters move, so it helps to explain what some of their problems are. Knowing this, we understand some of the motivation for their actions, and this heightens our awareness of the situation. In other words, thinking about setting can take us into the whole complex experience, and that's what it ought to do. After having made the first couple of observations, we should find that we can't ignore the other elements and their combinations. To the extent that this is true the approach has been helpful. It is a failure when the reader plods determinedly along looking neither to the right nor to the left. If he stolidly traces, say, character from beginning to end, he knows as much about the story as the tourist who drives through the Canadian Rockies with his eyes fixed only on the road before him.

To put it differently, the elements are important because thinking about them helps us to ask key questions. What is this character like? Why does he do this? How does he feel toward the other characters? What produced this situation? What imaginative structure can best be created from the various details? Trying to answer such questions takes the reader directly into the story and helps him to move through its structured experience.

The best reason that can be urged for doing this is that one's enjoyment increases proportionally with one's skill, and to enjoy is better than not to enjoy. This is the premise on which this book is based and for the sake of which we ask that you try our method.

Sequence and the Structure of Fiction

Any work of fiction has an order or arrangement of scenes. The reader begins with the first words, and moves from point to point according to a sequential arrangement. This can be divided into sections or parts, each of which is relatively distinct and forms a single stage.

The reason for dividing a work into sections rests on the simple assumption that a work of art, among other things, is a structure. The best way to comprehend any structure is to be aware of each of its parts and their relationships to one another.

9

The smallest unit of fiction is the word, each of which is important to the sensitive reader because words are the only doors by which he can enter the story.

Words do two kinds of things. They carry information, and they stimulate emotional responses. The writer of an article for a scientific journal would probably choose words with low emotive power. Whenever possible, he would shift into the language of mathematics, whose symbols are sometimes called "pure," since they don't trigger for most of us any emotional response at all. It doesn't follow from this that a writer of fiction or poetry necessarily chooses words with high emotive power. Some modern writers use unemotive words in an attempt to convey their images or scenes more sharply, trusting that the latter will have far greater explosive power because they are clearly and simply presented.

Whatever his choice, the writer has only the printed word to communicate through, and the reader must be keenly aware of it. As he reads, he mines each word, responding to both the idea it conveys and the emotions it triggers. This is the reader's first step in his imaginative recreation of a work of fiction. Like most first steps, this one is obvious, but none the less important.

This is why in the sample stories we ask questions about specific words. We could ask a great many more. Ideally, one ought to weigh the value of every word. After all, that's the way the story was written—word by word—but that would make this book far too cumbersome. Though the individual words are crucial, there are other things to consider as well, such as the larger units made by groups of words.

Words are not simply piled on top of each other like bricks to make a wall. The meanings of individual words as well as the emotive power of each are strongly affected by the relationship of each word to the other words in the sentence. Take, for example, the different meanings and the different emotional values of the word "ball" in the following sentences:

1
Teddy's favorite toy is a ball.
2
Did we ever have a ball!
3
Let us roll all our strength and all
Our sweetness up into one ball.

As the meanings and values of single words are affected by other words and different grammatical patterns, the meanings and values of sentences are shaped by other sentences in the paragraph and even by surrounding paragraphs.

There are structural units of fiction larger than words or sentences or paragraphs. In a drama they are called scenes; in a novel they are called chapters; in a short story we will call them sections.

Section. Breaking a story down into sections is far from simple, and your decision about what constitutes a section will be debatable. In fact, you ought to discuss the reasons for your particular sectioning. Through debate, you will find that your ideas about the story become clearer.

You could say that "Sredni Vashtar" divides into as many sections as there are words, but obviously that won't get you anywhere. It's almost as useless to say there are only two: the first leading up to Mrs. De Ropp's visit to the shed, and then the aftermath. The best answer—that is, the one which most helps the reader to see the dramatic pattern—lies somewhere between these extremes. We think there are seven. We don't pretend that we are absolutely right and that you, if you disagree, will be absolutely wrong. It isn't a matter of right and wrong so much as what is most helpful to understanding the story.

A section can be defined as a passage all of whose details work toward the production of a single general impression or state of mind in the reader. But how can these sections be discovered in any given piece of fiction? There is no mathematical formula which can be rigidly applied, but there are guidelines.

You ought to read the story through quickly the first time. Then go back to the beginning and start reading slowly and carefully asking yourself what mood or feeling the details are working to produce. When you are able to define that to yourself, watch for what seems a significant change. If, for example, the story begins with a description of the setting, the introduction of a character probably signals the beginning of section two. A shift in physical setting and characters usually begins a new section. Often the author himself signals this with a break in the text or with a transitional phrase like "meanwhile back at the ranch. . . ." However, most divisions are more subtle. A new section may begin with any event that changes the situation. It may be a character's decision to do something or go somewhere, or he may simply change his attitude toward his situation. These are the kinds of things that usually mark divisions, but there is no way of forecasting what will do it in any particular story. The crucial thing to remember is that each significant change produces a change in the reader's response, so the sensitive reader keeps one eye sharply trained on the text and the other as sharply on his own response to it. When his response changes—an increase of suspense, a new kind of concern for a character, or a new sense of satisfaction or sudden relief—something in the text has triggered it, and another section may have begun.

Probably the best way of clarifying these general instructions is by applying them.

JAMES THURBER   THE BEAR WHO LET IT ALONE

I

In the woods of the Far West there once lived a brown bear who could take it or let it alone. He would go into a bar where they sold mead, a fermented drink made of honey, and he would have just two drinks. Then he would put some money on the bar and say, "See what the bears in the back room will have," and he would go home.

II

But finally he took to drinking by himself most of the day. He would reel home at night, kick over the umbrella stand, knock down the bridge lamps, and ram his elbows through the windows. Then he would collapse on the floor and lie there until he went to sleep. His wife was greatly distressed and his children were frightened.

III

At length the bear saw the error of his ways and began to reform. In the end he became a famous teetotaller and a persistent temperance lecturer. He would tell everybody that came to his house about the awful effects of drink, and he would boast about how strong and well he had become since he gave up touching the stuff.

IV

To demonstrate this, he would stand on his head and on his hands and he would turn cartwheels in the house, kicking over the umbrella stand, knocking down the bridge lamps, and ramming his elbows through the windows. Then he would lie down on the floor, tired by his healthful exercise, and go to sleep. His wife was greatly distressed and his children were very frightened.

MORAL: You might as well fall flat on your face as lean over too far backward.

Section I creates the impression of a good, sound, lower middle-class bear. A dependable worker, neither too much a company man nor a troublemaker, he is probably liked and respected by his boss and by the community. He's not too snooty to be seen in a common bar and, though he doesn't drink heavily himself, he doesn't mind buying a round for the bears in the backroom where most of the old souses hang out. He's the sort of bear who keeps his house painted, the grass cut, and has lots of friends—in short, an all-around good citizen and good fellow.

Then trouble strikes. For no apparent reason, he isolates himself from his friends and takes to heavy, solitary drinking. He rolls home and smashes up that neat, well-kept house. His wife is miserable and confused. The children are frightened at the change in their father who is too drunk to play catch with them in the backyard as he used to. The main impression here is confusion, disorder, unhappiness, and disaster. The passage contains a significant change. It creates an entirely different impression from the orderly normality of the opening, and this therefore makes it Section II.

13

In the next passage our hero has miraculously reformed. All ought to be well again. Though it ought to be, our impression isn't quite the same as that created by Section I. The word "persistent" is troubling. A "persistent" temperance lecturer doesn't wait for invitations to speak. The good fellow of Section I may have become a bore. And then, too, he "boasts" about his new-found virtue. For his family's sake we are glad that he has turned over a new leaf, but we aren't altogether easy about it. The distress of Section II has been replaced by an uneasy hope, identifying this passage as Section III.

Section IV robs us of any sense of relief or hope. Disaster has struck again, this time from that inflated virtue we were concerned about in Section III.

Dividing the fable into sections should prepare you to see its structure—the order or sequence in which the sections are arranged. So far, we have only defined the things that are ordered. Before discussing the effect of their particular arrangement, it is necessary to examine the idea of sequence itself.

Sequence. Sequence is order in time, but it's difficult to think about order apart from things that are ordered. Because it's easier to talk about things than relationships, discussions of sequence run a real and constant danger of ending up as discussions of the things in sequence and not about sequence itself. Although sequence is very hard to talk about, it is also extremely important, so we must try.

Some sequences appear to be all but meaningless—at least we don't examine them for significance. For example, the sun shone Monday morning. The afternoon was cloudy and the evening warm. The temperature dropped about midnight, and a breeze sprang up out of the northwest. By seven o'clock, the wind was quite strong, and the lake was whitecapping.

These changes might be interesting to a meteorologist, but most of us would probably live through them without looking for their causes or asking whether they formed a pattern. We are emotionally committed to other sequences, but we seldom ask that they be justified. How many would eat unquestioningly through a dinner which began with pie à la mode, followed by mashed potatoes, then cheese, next broccoli, then soup and roast beef last? Is there any compelling reason why a dinner should not follow this order? Why should not courtship follow marriage? In some cultures it does and with, they say, equal success. Why should we be forced to study geometry when so many of us have no intention of ever building a bridge? If we changed our minds, presumably we could learn geometry then. Probably a major portion of our lives is spent plodding uncritically through sequences whose rationale we seldom consider and whose significance we do not think to ask ourselves about. This habit is an obstacle not only to living well, but to reading well.

More than anything else, the sequence carries the vision in fiction. The relationship between sequence and meaning is obvious when we look at the letters which make up the printed word. Take the letters "s," "a," "r," "t." In that order they spell "sart," a combination we aren't familiar with. Arrange the same letters in a different order, and they make "star," or "rats," or "arts," or "tars." The objects or ideas that these different spellings refer to are not remotely similar. We wouldn't confuse a bunch of rats with a star, nor a star with arts, and so on, but each of these separate and very distinct things is referred to by the same collection of letters. It is the sequence of the letters which determines meaning.

The same thing is true with fiction. Sequence of sections determines vision. Of course, a section of a story is far more complicated and suggestive than a single letter of the alphabet. We can read a word like "star" with speed and assurance because we are completely familiar with each of its sections or letters. We can't read a piece of serious fiction with anything like that confidence because we are not familiar with its sections. We have, in fact, never met them before because they don't exist anywhere except in that story. Each story is its own unique experience, and we haven't had that experience until we have identified its sections and felt the force of each—that is, until we have produced in ourselves the state of mind which each section conveys. Then we can feel the power of their order which drives us to understand the writer's vision or, more simply, to feel about the world as he does.

As an illustration of this, look again at the first section of Thurber's fable. The impression or state of mind which it creates might be described like this: "I feel good; everything's all right because that bear's got the world under control, and he's doing beautifully." Section II produces a very different impression. "I feel upset. There is confusion, disorder, fear." That might be what we would say while trying to talk about Section II separately, without reference to Section I. But, of course, the second section does follow the first, and the state which is produced is affected by that fact. In other words, the sequence matters. Our concern in Section II is deepened because we have moved to it from the sense of well-being, almost gaiety, of Section I. We might feel very little distress for the bear and his family if we read Section II first. We might feel that confusion and disorder are the normal state of things, so a disrupted home wouldn't move us much. Another way of putting the point is that it doesn't hurt to stand on the sidewalk. It would hurt, though, to be suddenly dropped five feet through the air onto that sidewalk. In the order in which Thurber writes the story, Section II is the psychic equivalent of such a drop. A well-ordered, comfortable, secure world has suddenly collapsed. The once competent, cheerful bear has become a helpless victim of his own unsuspected weakness. There seems no hope of recapturing that earlier happiness.

15

Section III retrieves us from sadness. The bear reforms. Hurrah! Things are going to be great again!

Just as Section II was more depressing because it was a fall from the happiness of Section I, so Section III gains a special gloss of promise and relief because it unexpectedly raises the spirits from the depths of Section II—so much that we suppress the warning signals of "persistent" and "boasts."

Then comes Section IV.

Down, down, down we go in surprise and dismay as the reformed bear goes through the identical catalog of misdemeanors which he used to commit while drunk and his wife and children, along with the reader, feel even worse than they did at the end of Section II. The reform for which they had then hoped came, but their hopes for what it would bring were smashed. What is left for them to hope for?

Thinking about the sequence of these sections of this fable makes its dramatic pattern or structure clear, that is, we can chart the states of mind through which we are moved, and we can see how each successive one is given special and important qualities by those that precede it. We could even diagram that pattern. It would look something like a capital "M" with the second peak probably rising higher than the first, and that would represent the shape of the experience which we have recreated. Section I takes us up the vertical line to good spirits and happiness. Section II brings us down hard to dismay. Section III raises us suddenly to a higher peak of good cheer, and Section IV, because the fall is greater, smashes us down.

Though we have exaggerated the extent of our emotional involvement with the fable, we have not exaggerated the pattern which sequence creates. The basic pattern of raising and then dashing hopes which this fable illustrates is also the pattern of Sophocles' *Oedipus Rex*, but there is a great difference in the degree or intensity of the reader's involvement. Thurber doesn't mean us to take his story with deadly seriousness. His setting is a world of half reality and half fantasy. The reality consists in what is done and what is felt. The fantasy is that the characters are bears who are doing and feeling what men do and feel. Though partly in jest, the story is also partly serious. It has a meaning which Thurber restates in the moral.

16   The moral isn't actually a part of the story. It's Thurber's statement of the general truth that the story reveals. A good part of Thurber's humor lies in the moral he draws from his tiny stories, but most writers of good fiction don't try to state their moral or what we would call their vision. Their reasons for not doing so are twofold. First, if they have any artistic self-respect, they have to assume that the story conveys that vision, so why bother trying to state it again? Second, no single statement could contain all the complexities of the story. Besides, mere statement of a truth doesn't emotionally involve a reader, and the mere acknowledgment of a truth is not the same as feeling it. Therefore, the only way a writer could restate his vision would be to repeat the story.

Even in the case of Thurber's fable, it might be worth asking whether the moral actually does contain all the force of even so brief a tale.

Vision

You will recall our definition of fiction: "a piece of writing which presents a direct appeal to the reader's imagination through a sectioned sequence of details which reveal particular characters in particular settings, acting and interacting with each other in relation to certain events and situations—all of which taken together in this particular combination conveys a vision of what human life is like."

We have so far tried to define all but one of the various terms in this definition— the term *vision*—although we have been using it throughout our discussion. It is such an important concept that it is impossible to talk about fiction without referring to it. But it is so difficult to define with accuracy that we have saved it for last.

Art is a comment about what it feels like to be alive. All comments are legitimate, and they may run all the way from "I've got all the answers to life and its problems," to "I don't understand one bit about life, not one bit." Those sentences are comments on life, but they aren't art. The main reason they aren't is that they tell rather than show. It is so much easier to explain our feelings that most of us settle for doing that, but we all feel the need to have others experience what we experience. Maybe you have come into the kitchen and found your sister working her way through a large piece of double-Dutch chocolate layer cake, and you asked, "How's the cake?" If she felt as most of us do most of the time, she might say, "pretty good," and go on chewing and licking the icing off her fingers. If, on the other hand, her sensitivities were so sharpened by the pleasure of that cake, if it had raised her to that pitch of excitement in which she wished you to feel the soft, cold icing on her lips, the gentle submission of its texture between her teeth, and the explosion of rich, dark streams of taste along her tongue—if she wanted you to share her continuous shiver of complex delights, she would realize that there could be no explanation equivalent to the experience, so she would give you a piece with the artist's unspoken request, "Feel what I feel."

17

However richly sensuous and evocative, the eating of a piece of cake is a less complex experience than being in love. One's beloved has a far greater number and variety of attractions, and he or she fulfills or seems to hold out the promise of fulfilling a much greater range of needs. The process of falling in love, the being in love, and the falling out of love is a sequence of experiences so complex and so powerful that it can and frequently does shape our view of what life is all about. Though more complicated and more profound, such a sequence has a great deal in common with the eating of a piece of cake. Both are experiences; neither can be explained, but if we have the artist's need for communication, and if we have his talents, each experience can be conveyed through symbolic representation. The writer translates his experience into the symbols of print, but there they lie fallow until the sensitive reader retranslates those symbols into experience. Then the poem or story has become part of the reader's life. By definition, a piece of good fiction is the record of important experience, the kind which makes a difference to how one thinks and feels about things. Having brought back to life the writer's experience, the reader stands, so to speak, where the writer stood. He looks at the world through the writer's eyes and sees it through an emotionally charged atmosphere and in the light of what has just happened. He is in a position to say to the writer, "I have seen, I have felt, so I understand."

What he understands is the writer's vision, the way the writer looked at life. That vision cannot be stated in simple terms. It is too complex, too deeply charged with emotional tensions. That doesn't mean, however, that it can't be talked about. In fact, it ought to be talked about because it is only through such talk that we can get a sense of how each of us has read the story.

Vision is the product of the combination of all the other ingredients of fiction. As with the others, the force or importance of vision depends solely upon how completely the reader apprehends it, how successfully he makes it a part of his own experience. We are so familiar with our experience that we seldom inquire into what it implies about life. To understand fiction, however, one must read more attentively than one lives.

The meaning of a story isn't to be found tucked away in a single sentence or paragraph, so it's no use looking for that kind of answer. In fact, the question, "What does this story mean?" isn't even the right question. Phrased in that way, it makes the piece of fiction sound like a complex riddle, and riddles are to be solved by the exercise of pure or mere intellect, and a story is not. A story is not to be solved at all. It is to be experienced through the imagination, and from the experience the trained reader has a sense of what the writer's world is like. This is why the term "vision" comes closer to what we are talking about than does "theme," or "meaning," or "idea." These words are too closely connected with thought, limited too narrowly to rational processes. A story almost always will express a thought, but that thought is so intimately fused with feeling that it is impossible to separate the two without doing injustice to the writer and to his work.

The fact that you have imaginatively entered the world of the writer, that you have experienced his vision, does not mean that you will necessarily agree that it is an accurate vision, one that you fully accept. One of the values of fiction, and for that matter, all imaginative literature, is that it offers us the opportunity to experience the world momentarily in the skin of another. Although we must ultimately return to our own, this experience—available to those with a disciplined imagination—broadens our own vision. To see beyond our own confined perspectives makes the experience of literature a valuable one, one well worth taking the time and effort required to make it possible.

PART TWO: STORIES AND QUESTIONS FOR
                             INTENSIVE ANALYSIS

Each of the following four stories is first reprinted in its entirety; we then repeat
it divided into sections. A series of questions accompanies each section to call
your attention to the details, without which your imaginative reconstruction of
the story would be vague and imprecise.

First read the story through, fairly quickly, to get a sense of it as a whole. Then
go to the sectioned version, read the first section, and try to answer the questions
on that section. We strongly recommend that you *write* the answers. The last
question on each section requires that you write at least one paragraph. It is extremely important that you do this, because it is difficult to keep all the significant details of a story in mind without a record to refer to.

This paragraph should include not only the details but your reactions to them,
and it is your reactions that will ultimately form your sense of what the story
is about.

At the end of each story you will find several topics which your instructor may
use as the basis for assigning papers. If a paper is not assigned, we urge you to
think over the topics anyway, because they will help you organize your feelings
and ideas into a coherent structure.

As an illustration, we have answered the questions for "Cat in the Rain." With
this as with the other stories, we don't pretend to have asked all the questions it is
possible to ask, and, after study, you may disagree with our treatment of those
we have asked and answered. It should, however, give you an idea of what we
have in mind.

20 There were only two Americans stopping at the hotel. They did not know any of the people they passed on the stairs on their way to and from their room. Their room was on the second floor facing the sea. It also faced the public garden and the war monument. There were big palms and green benches in the public garden. In the good weather there was always an artist with his easel. Artists liked the way the palms grew and the bright colors of the hotels facing the gardens and the sea. Italians came from a long way off to look up at the war monument. It was made of bronze and glistened in the rain. It was raining. The rain dripped from the palm trees. Water stood in pools on the gravel paths. The sea broke in a long line in the rain and slipped back down the beach to come up and break again in a long line in the rain. The motor cars were gone from the square by the war monument. Across the square in the doorway of the café a waiter stood looking out at the empty square.

The American wife stood at the window looking out. Outside right under their window a cat was crouched under one of the dripping green tables. The cat was trying to make herself so compact that she would not be dripped on.

"I'm going down and get that kitty," the American wife said.

"I'll do it," her husband offered from the bed.

"No, I'll get it. The poor kitty out trying to keep dry under a table."

The husband went on reading, lying propped up with the two pillows at the foot of the bed.

"Don't get wet," he said.

The wife went downstairs and the hotel owner stood up and bowed to her as she passed the office. His desk was at the far end of the office. He was an old man and very tall.

"Il piove," the wife said. She liked the hotel-keeper.

"Si, si, Signora, brutto tempo. It is very bad weather."

---

*

He stood behind his desk in the far end of the dim room. The wife liked him.
She liked the deadly serious way he received any complaints. She liked his dignity. She liked the way he wanted to serve her. She liked the way he felt about
being a hotel-keeper. She liked his old, heavy face and big hands.

Liking him she opened the door and looked out. It was raining harder. A man
in a rubber cape was crossing the empty square to the café. The cat would be
around to the right. Perhaps she could go along under the eaves. As she stood in
the doorway an umbrella opened behind her. It was the maid who looked after
their room.

"You must not get wet," she smiled, speaking Italian. Of course, the hotelkeeper had sent her.

With the maid holding the umbrella over her, she walked along the gravel path
until she was under their window. The table was there, washed bright green in
the rain, but the cat was gone. She was suddenly disappointed. The maid looked
up at her.

"Ha perduto qualque cosa, Signora?"

"There was a cat," said the American girl.

"A cat?"

"Si, il gatto."

"A cat?" the maid laughed. "A cat in the rain?"

"Yes," she said, "under the table." Then, "Oh, I wanted it so much. I wanted
a kitty."

When she talked English the maid's face tightened.

"Come, Signora," she said. "We must get back inside. You will be wet."

"I suppose so," said the American girl.

They went back along the gravel path and passed in the door. The maid stayed
outside to close the umbrella. As the American girl passed the office, the padrone
bowed from his desk. Something felt very small and tight inside the girl. The
padrone made her feel very small and at the same time really important. She had
a momentary feeling of being of supreme importance. She went on up the stairs.
She opened the door of the room. George was on the bed, reading.

"Did you get the cat?" he asked, putting the book down.

"It was gone."

"Wonder where it went to," he said, resting his eyes from reading.

She sat down on the bed.

"I wanted it so much," she said. "I don't know why I wanted it so much.
I wanted that poor kitty. It isn't any fun to be a poor kitty out in the rain."

George was reading again.

She went over and sat in front of the mirror of the dressing table looking at
herself with the hand glass. She studied her profile, first one side and then the
other. Then she studied the back of her head and her neck.

"Don't you think it would be a good idea if I let my hair grow out?" she asked,
looking at her profile again.

George looked up and saw the back of her neck, clipped close like a boy's.

"I like it the way it is."

"I get so tired of it," she said. "I get so tired of looking like a boy."

George shifted his position in the bed. He hadn't looked away from her since she started to speak.

"You look pretty darn nice," he said.

She laid the mirror down on the dresser and went over to the window and looked out. It was getting dark.

"I want to pull my hair back tight and smooth and make a big knot at the back that I can feel," she said. "I want to have a kitty to sit on my lap and purr when I stroke her."

"Yeah?" George said from the bed.

"And I want to eat at a table with my own silver and I want candles. And I want it to be spring, and I want to brush my hair out in front of a mirror and I want a kitty and I want some new clothes."

"Oh, shut up and get something to read," George said. He was reading again.

His wife was looking out of the window. It was quite dark now and still raining in the palm trees.

"Anyway, I want a cat," she said. "I want a cat. I want a cat now. If I can't have long hair or any fun, I can have a cat."

George was not listening. He was reading his book. His wife looked out of the window where the light had come on in the square.

Someone knocked at the door.

"Avanti," George said. He looked up from his book.

In the doorway stood the maid. She held a big tortoise-shell cat pressed tight against her and swung down against her body.

"Excuse me," she said, "the padrone asked me to bring this for the Signora."

SECTION I

There were only two Americans stopping at the hotel. They did not know any of the people they passed on the stairs on their way to and from their room. Their room was on the second floor facing the sea. It also faced the public garden and the war monument. There were big palms and green benches in the public garden. In the good weather there was always an artist with his easel. Artists liked the way the palms grew and the bright colors of the hotels facing the gardens and the sea. Italians came from a long way off to look up at the war monument. It was made of bronze and glistened in the rain. It was raining. The rain dripped from the palm trees. Water stood in pools on the gravel paths. The sea broke in a long line in the rain and slipped back down the beach to come up and break again in a long line in the rain. The motor cars were gone from the square by the war monument. Across the square in the doorway of the café a waiter stood looking out at the empty square.

SECTION I: QUESTIONS AND ANSWERS

1

What do the first two sentences tell us about the American couple?

Answer: They are isolated, friendless. Since they went to no place except their room at the hotel, they apparently are not sightseers. Probably they are merely stopping here on their way to somewhere else. Since they have neither friends nor interest in the town, the hotel room is the center of their lives at this particular time.

2

What is the main difference between the public square with the garden and war monument in good weather and at the time of the story?

Answer: In good weather the square is rich with color, full of people, a happy center of cultural life. The rain has driven the people away, and now it is damp and empty.

3

What similarities are there between the public square in the rain and the situation of the Americans?

Answer: The square is empty, lonely, forlorn, and the Americans appear to be in the same condition.

4

What does the rain and the repetitious breaking of the sea add to the setting?

Answer: They suggest a monotonous, dreary world.

5

In a paragraph, describe the setting* as defined by the details of this section.

Answer: All the details work to produce an atmosphere of dreariness, vacancy, and loneliness. The American couple are isolated by their nationality. The weather has turned the populous, gay, and beautiful square into a blank monotone. The people have not

23

---

*

See discussion of *setting*, pp. 5-6.

simply retreated momentarily to the shelter of cafés or the waiter who stands idly surveying the emptiness would be busy serving his customers. The place has an air of weary desolation with the regular, meaningless breaking of the sea and the dripping of the rain. The atmosphere created is heavy, oppressive, empty, and this makes "their room" all the more important to the American couple. If they are to find any happiness or pleasure in this town, they must find it with each other in the seclusion of their room.

SECTION II

The American wife stood at the window looking out. Outside right under their window a cat was crouched under one of the dripping green tables. The cat was trying to make herself so compact that she would not be dripped on.
"I'm going down and get that kitty," the American wife said.
"I'll do it," her husband offered from the bed.
"No, I'll get it. The poor kitty out trying to keep dry under a table."
The husband went on reading, lying propped up with the two pillows at the foot of the bed.
"Don't get wet," he said.

SECTION II: QUESTIONS AND ANSWERS

1

In what way is it consistent with the setting that the woman is referred to as "the American wife" rather than by her name?

Answer: She has no more specificity than the town. We don't know its name or precise location, only that it is on the Italian coast. The phrase "American wife" may also suggest a contrast between European and American marriages.

2

Why is her attention attracted by the cat and its predicament?

Answer: The cat is apparently the only living thing in the square. Its discomfort perhaps arouses her maternal instinct. Then, too, she may unconsciously see similarities between the position of the cat and her own.

3

What does the husband's offer from the bed indicate about the couple's relationship?

Answer: His offer is an empty gesture. Since he doesn't get up to do her the favor, it is clear his offer is only half hearted, but he apparently feels that since she is a woman, he should, as a man, offer to save her the discomfort of getting the cat. Their relationship must be at least superficially amicable, or he wouldn't even have paid lip service to the tradition of man's courteous protection. But since he doesn't move, he can't take this tradition very seriously. Instead of lying in the normal position, he lies reading with his head toward the foot of the bed, suggesting an unwillingness or incapacity to assume the role of a man.

4

What connection between the wife and the "poor kitty" is suggested by the husband's casual remark, "Don't get wet"?

Answer: He is willing to express concern for his wife, but not prepared to do anything about it. He can't seriously imagine that she could go out in the rain without getting wet, but his masculine conscience is satisfied by telling her not to.

5

Sum up in a paragraph the relationship between the situation* of the husband and wife and the setting.

Answer: The setting and the situation of the husband and wife blend perfectly. Both convey the sense of vacant hoplessness. Before the weather turned, the town was gay, lovely, and exciting, and the romance that preceded the marriage of the Americans was probably all those things, too. Now that the rain has come, the town is empty and oppressive, and after the ceremony, the marriage bed has become a place where the husband, reversing his position, has taken to reading and from which he makes an occasional empty gesture which acknowledges his wife to be a woman. Both the situation and setting convey a strong sense of emptiness and isolation. The only spark is the wife's sympathy for the cat and her resolution to help it.

*

See discussion of *situation*, pp. 7-8.

SECTION III

The wife went downstairs and the hotel owner stood up and bowed to her as she passed the office. His desk was at the far end of the office. He was an old man and very tall.

"Il piove," the wife said. She liked the hotel-keeper.

"Si, si, Signora, brutto tempo. It is very bad weather."

He stood behind his desk in the far end of the dim room. The wife liked him. She liked the deadly serious way he received any complaints. She liked his dignity. She liked the way he wanted to serve her. She liked the way he felt about being a hotel-keeper. She liked his old, heavy face and big hands.

SECTION III: QUESTIONS AND ANSWERS

1

What impression is conveyed about the hotelkeeper by the details used to describe him?

Answer: He is a courteous, attentive, thoughtful man. Since he listens seriously to complaints, communication with him is obviously possible, and his big hands imply that he is capable of action. He is a man of stature, with dignity, assurance, clearly competent.

2

Why does the wife like the hotelkeeper?

Answer: He shows an active respect and concern for her and her needs. Also, he treats her as if she were a woman and therefore deserving of special attention. He is romantically masculine.

3

How does the hotelkeeper differ from her husband?

Answer: The hotelkeeper seems all that her husband is not. Though at the other end of the room, the hotelkeeper rises when she enters. There may even be a play on the word "office" in the sense of job. The hotelkeeper's office or task does not place him in an intimate relationship with her, and yet he performs it with more attention and concern than her husband performs his. By comparison, her husband seems almost invalided or emasculated as he lies upside down on their bed merely reading.

4

In a paragraph, discuss the significance of this section's immediately following the previous section: What is achieved by this sequence?*

Answer: The primary effect is that of sharp contrast. The hotelkeeper is so different, treats her so differently from her husband.

---

*

See discussion of *sequence* in "The Bear Who let it Alone," pp. 13-16.

The torpor and vacuity of the preceding sections are broken. She feels something clear and positive. The word "liked" appears seven times in this section, emphasizing the reality of her response to this other man. The reader becomes aware that she is not dead to her sexuality even if her husband is. The depth of her need for a man is revealed by this sequence—first the husband's in-effectiveness and then the hotelkeeper's dig-nified manliness to which she responds so actively. The American wife is bound to make the comparison with her husband, and the contrast must produce some kind of explosion.

27

SECTION IV

Liking him she opened the door and looked out. It was raining harder. A man in a rubber cape was crossing the empty square to the café. The cat would be around to the right. Perhaps she could go along under the eaves. As she stood in the doorway an umbrella opened behind her. It was the maid who looked after their room.

"You must not get wet," she smiled, speaking Italian. Of course, the hotel-keeper had sent her.

With the maid holding the um-brella over her, she walked along the gravel path until she was under their window. The table was there, washed bright green in the rain, but the cat was gone. She was suddenly disappointed. The maid looked up at her.

"Ha perduto qualque cosa, Signora?"

"There was a cat," said the Ameri-can girl.

"A cat?"

"Si, il gatto."

"A cat?" the maid laughed. "A cat in the rain?"

"Yes," she said, "under the table." Then, "Oh, I wanted it so much. I wanted a kitty."

SECTION IV: QUESTIONS AND ANSWERS

1

What is suggested by the hotelkeeper's taking the responsibility for keeping the wife dry?

Answer: It proves that her estimate of the hotelkeeper was accurate. Though he is a distant figure, her comfort and well-being matter to him. He is a person of authority who orders that she shall be spared the dis-comfort of getting wet. His unostentatious order differs sharply from her husband's, "Don't get wet."

2

What is the effect of her being referred to as "the American girl" instead of "the American wife"?

Answer: It emphasizes her youth, depend-ence, and raises romantic possibilities, which don't exist in her relationship with her hus-band. It also indicates that her marriage has been unfulfilling and has not helped her to mature or grow.

3

Why is she disappointed that the cat is gone?

Answer: Having, holding, actively loving that cat offered a momentary escape from the vague, half-conscious frustrations of her relationship with her husband. It reveals her own need to be cared for in the same way.

When she talked English the maid's face tightened.

"Come, Signora," she said. "We must get back inside. You will be wet."

"I suppose so," said the American girl.

They went back along the gravel path and passed in the door. The maid stayed outside to close the umbrella. As the American girl passed the office, the padrone bowed from his desk. Something felt very small and tight inside the girl. The padrone made her feel very small and at the same time really important. She had a momentary feeling of being of supreme importance. She went on up the stairs. She opened the door of the room. George was on the bed, reading.

4

In Italian, *padrone* is a word for father, master, or boss. Why is the hotelkeeper now referred to as "the padrone"?

Answer: He is all those things to her since he has done with dignity what her husband should have. He is a person who takes care of her, a superior, a power figure, a man.

5

What do the three descriptions of her feelings in the padrone's presence reveal about the girl's emotional needs?

Answer: The first sentence suggests pregnancy. That she wants a child is also hinted at by her feelings for the cat. In the padrone's presence, this wish seems to be fulfilled. The second sentence shows her need for dependence on a larger, stronger person, and the padrone succeeds in making her feel this while at the same time making her feel as if she were someone of consequence. The third sentence acts as a summary. Her real need is to be loved, to matter to someone more than anything else in the world.

6

In the context of the details of this section, discuss in a paragraph the effect created by her entering the room to find George "on the bed, reading."

Answer: She begins the section in the mild glow of her liking for the hotelkeeper. By sending the maid with the umbrella, he becomes the padrone, and her pleasure and sense of security grow. This is broken when she finds the cat gone. Even the padrone could not prevent that sadness, and again she feels her isolation standing in the rain, the maid's face tightening as she tries to understand the American girl's language. Expressing herself even about the loss of a cat which was not hers causes her difficulty. How can she hope to convey the far deeper, more complex needs which she feels the force of, but can only half identify? Retreating from her disappointment, she goes inside again and falls under the warmth of

the padrone's personality. His presence reassures, comforts, even exalts her. All is well.
He becomes almost a masculine divinity
capable of satisfying all her feminine needs.
Then she opens the door to her marriage.
Behind it is her private and personal share
of masculine strength. He lies reading. She is
confronted by the contrast between George
and the padrone. What can she feel but
despair?

SECTION V

"Did you get the cat?" he asked,
putting the book down.

"It was gone."

"Wonder where it went to," he
said, resting his eyes from reading.

She sat down on the bed.

"I wanted it so much," she said. "I
don't know why I wanted it so
much. I wanted that poor kitty. It
isn't any fun to be a poor kitty out
in the rain."

George was reading again.

She went over and sat in front of
the mirror of the dressing table
looking at herself with the hand
glass. She studied her profile, first
one side and then the other. Then
she studied the back of her head and
her neck.

"Don't you think it would be a
good idea if I let my hair grow out?"
she asked, looking at her profile
again.

George looked up and saw the
back of her neck, clipped close like
a boy's.

"I like it the way it is."

"I get so tired of it," she said. "I
get so tired of looking like a boy."

George shifted his position in the
bed. He hadn't looked away from
her since she started to speak.

"You look pretty darn nice," he
said.

She laid the mirror down on the
dresser and went over to the window
and looked out. It was getting dark.

SECTION V: QUESTIONS AND ANSWERS   29

1

How does she respond to George's careless
reception?

Answer: Instead of blowing up or collapsing
in tears, she tells him that the cat was gone,
hoping that he might understand what this
meant to her. He doesn't. Trying to express
her own need to be held, comforted, and
loved, she goes over to sit on the bed beside
him. To rescue her, he doesn't even need
to get up, let alone go out into the rain. She
sits within easy reach, making her appeal,
waiting, and hoping for help. His response
to her plea is to return to his book. Rising,
she goes to the dressing table to study herself with a mirror as if searching for some
defect in her appearance that might explain
her failure to engage George's interest. Finally, she decides that she doesn't look enough
like a woman because of her short hair, and
she asks George if longer hair would make
her more attractive.

2

To what extent is George responsible for the
feelings his wife expresses when she says,
"It isn't any fun to be a poor kitty out in
the rain"?

Answer: As she identifies herself and her
condition with the cat and his predicament,
the wife is expressing her instinctive response that this kind of marriage is not the
world she is made for. She feels isolated,
frustrated, and with no prospect of emotional
or physiological fulfillment. George's lack

"I want to pull my hair back tight and smooth and make a big knot at the back that I can feel," she said. "I want to have a kitty to sit on my lap and purr when I stroke her."

"Yeah?" George said from the bed.

"And I want to eat at a table with my own silver and I want candles. And I want it to be spring and I want to brush my hair out in front of a mirror and I want a kitty and I want some new clothes."

"Oh, shut up and get something to read," George said. He was reading again.

of sensitivity to her needs is largely responsible for this, but some of the burden rests on the conventions of American society. By contrasting the American and the European male's attitude toward women, Hemingway seems to suggest that the American fails to acknowledge the personhood of woman. George is content to consider his wife as an object and an attractive one, but he can't accept the fact that she has human needs which it is his responsibility to satisfy.

3

When she says, "I get so tired of it, . . . I get so tired of looking like a boy," what is she trying to express?

Answer: She is struggling to say a great many only half-understood things. Perhaps the main one is dissatisfaction with her position as merely sexual object. Since her relations with her husband have been only sexual, they have been barren, producing neither children nor any joint emotional development. There is no love, no marriage. Likening herself to a boy, she hints that their relationship might as well have been a homosexual one. Her boyish appearance suggests a sameness with her husband, and she longs to be sufficiently different in his eyes to justify the establishment of a whole new set of relationships that build upon but transcend the merely sexual. George, on the other hand, prefers that she look like a boy because it implies no special demands made upon him.

4

What image of herself and the life she would like to lead is created by the strongly asserted detailed list of wishes she now expresses?

Answer: The implicit appeal of her question having failed, she gets up to look from the window of her present position into the world outside or into the future. It is growing dark, and this triggers her verbal explosion of "I want, I want, and I want!" The hair-do she would like to have suggests the European mother figure with the kitty as a symbolic child. She longs for the stability

of roots plus the thrill of being eternally
pursued. She wants the excitement of
romance minus its instability, the security of
family life without boredom. She wants, in
short, the impossible, but the knowledge of
its impossibility in no way assuages the intensity of her yearning. The fact of her need
is so real, so huge as to dwarf the irrationali-
ties of its expression.

5

What does George's response indicate about
his interest in and capacity to satisfy her
needs?

Answer: George's careless "yeah?" shows
that he has at least partly heard, but it expresses no sympathy for her condition or
any intention of helping her.

When she continues, instead of making
any effort to understand or even showing
her any sympathy, he merely gets annoyed.
Perhaps the superficial contradictions of her
list irritate him, but if they are the cause of
his annoyance, it is only further proof of
his insensitivity. It seems more likely that
he merely resents demands which, if he took
them seriously, would require self-criticism
and a reassessment of what the relations
between man and woman ought to be. He
would have to admit that love implied
responsibilities, and he is either unable or
unwilling to concede this. Instead of dealing
with the problem, he simply tells her to
"shut up and get something to read"—in
other words, "don't waste time with life;
escape."

6

Sum up in a paragraph the picture of this
couple's relationship revealed by the details
of this section.

Answer: Superficially, their relationship
seems unremarkable—a dependent wife who
is mildly attractive to her husband. The first
bloom of newly-wed excitement has faded,
and the wife is vaguely conscious of deep
problems. The main one is a lack of real
communication. She does not know how to
reach George to tell him of her deeply felt
but only half-understood needs. She wants

to be mistress, mother, wife—all things that are woman and womanly. Unable to bridge the gap that separates them, she is left hopeless and alone. Though George, too, is alone, he seems unaware of it or else he doesn't mind. If he does mind, he has given up any hope of conquering that problem. He seems to be even less aware of his condition than his wife is of hers and so perhaps deserves more sympathy. He seems frozen in the attitude of escape. Though each is within arm's length of the other, there seems no possibility of spanning that gulf. Their prospect is as hopeless as the dripping, empty square that darkens outside their window.

SECTION VI

His wife was looking out of the window. It was quite dark now and still raining in the palm trees.

"Anyway, I want a cat," she said, "I want a cat. I want a cat now. If I can't have long hair or any fun, I can have a cat."

George was not listening. He was reading his book. His wife looked out of the window where the light had come on in the square.

Someone knocked at the door.

"Avanti," George said. He looked up from his book.

In the doorway stood the maid. She held a big tortoise-shell cat pressed tight against her and swung down against her body.

"Excuse me," she said, "the padrone asked me to bring this for the Signora."

SECTION VI: QUESTIONS AND ANSWERS

1

What effect is created by this sequence: the wife's repeated demands for a cat, the light going on in the square, and the knock at the door?

Answer: The wife is not silenced by George's angry rejection of her appeal. She is going to go on wanting, needing, trying to speak. When the light goes on outside, it is as if the urgency of her speech commanded a responsive audience. This hint of an answer stirs hope in the reader for a miracle. Perhaps help is coming for her from somewhere. The sudden knock at the door intensifies this hope, and the entrance of the maid with the cat is the triumphant climax.

2

What is it, other than his wife's words, that George is not listening to?

Who is listening?

Answer: George isn't paying any attention to the fact that she is a human being with human needs. The padrone, though not literally listening to this particular speech of the wife's, is paying attention. She never told him personally that she wanted the cat, but he took the trouble to find out from the maid what took her out into the rain. He saw to it that she got what she wanted. His action demonstrates that not all men are like George, and that the wife's situation is not hopeless.

3

Does the padrone's action forecast any change in the relationship of the American couple?

Answer: Probably there will be a change, but it is impossible to say exactly what kind. Since the padrone has proved that other men will respond to the wife's needs, she might abandon all hope of her husband and take a lover or a succession of them. She might divorce George and remarry. On the other hand, perhaps jealousy might awaken George's sense of his own need for a more mature relationship with his wife. It seems more likely, however, that if he noticed his wife responding to the attention of other men, he would simply chalk it up to the fickleness of women. Since his wife couldn't be content with a trip to the Italian Riviera, what could he possibly do? With this defense, he would probably cross her off without suspecting that love means more than an expenses-paid trip to the Mediterranean.

4

In a paragraph, show how the events of this section are related to the events of the preceding sections. How does the sequence of events contribute to their meaning?

Answer: The climactic events of this section—and indeed of the entire story—is the entrance of the maid carrying the cat and her saying, "Excuse me, . . . the padrone asked me to bring this for the Signora." Almost every word is fraught with complex meanings because of what has gone before, so the speech acts as a kind of summary as well as giving a hopeful turn to our constantly growing sense of the wife's frustrations. The isolation of the American couple established at the beginning and developed throughout the story has been broken with the polite but firm "Excuse me." The "padrone"—father,

34

boss, master—exerts authority and gives orders that the American wife shall have her wish. He does with discretion what the recumbent George does not even acknowledge needs doing. More than a cat he sends her what the cat has come to stand for—a symbolic child with all the physical fulfillment of pregnancy and birth, the stability and roots of a family life, the chance to hold and love another creature and to be loved. It might be argued that the padrone doesn't realize the cat's importance, but this is irrelevant. The hotelkeeper exists in contrast with George, and the padrone accepts it as his responsibility that a woman under his care should have what she needs, and he provides it. George, whose responsibilities are far heavier, does not. If the story had opened with the presentation of the cat, the event would have been meaningless. What gives it power is our sympathy for the American wife which arises from our understanding of her situation. Then, too, the cat arrives immediately after the loss of all hope. Also, the incident gains force because it is an answer to the wife's cry, and it comes at a time when the wife and the reader have lost any hope for a reply. Section V ends on a note of despair. Also, much of the force of the incident comes from its taking us in an emotional direction counter to that of the rest of the story. The opening sets a stage of physical emptiness which is gradually developed into the profound isolation of both George and his wife. We feel this most acutely at the end of Section V. From the despair of Section V, the story swings sharply up toward hope with the snapping on of the light in the square, the knock at the door, the entrance of the maid with the cat, and finally her explanation. Loneliness, isolation, emptiness are not inevitable, then. People do hear each other's cries, and some do answer with help because there is such a thing as caring.

Cat in the Rain
Topics for Essays

NOTE. Whichever of these topics you write on and whatever the position you take, remember that your view must rest on an understanding of the details of the story. Your generalizations have to be supported by specific references to the text and by interpretation of those references. Any opinion which is unsupported by evidence is worthless, while any opinion supported by evidence must command respect.

1
Define the vision* of life expressed through the story and describe how the sequence, or the character, or the setting, or the situation, or any combination of these elements helps to communicate it.

2
What does the setting contribute to the wife's situation?

3
What is suggested in this story about the contrast between the attitudes of American men toward their women and those of European men?

4
What is the relationship of the title to the experience of the story?

5
Defend or attack the following statement: "The source of the trouble in this marriage is that George is interested in abstractions and his wife is interested in life."

---

*
See discussion of *vision*, pp. 16-18.

SAKI   SREDNI VASHTAR

36   Conradin was ten years old, and the doctor had pronounced his professional opinion that the boy would not live another five years. The doctor was silky and effete, and counted for little, but his opinion was endorsed by Mrs. De Ropp, who counted for nearly everything. Mrs. De Ropp was Conradin's cousin and guardian, and in his eyes she represented those three-fifths of the world that are necessary and disagreeable and real; the other two-fifths, in perpetual antagonism to the foregoing, were summed up in himself and his imagination. One of these days Conradin supposed he would succumb to the mastering pressure of wearisome necessary things—such as illnesses and coddling restrictions and drawn-out dulness. Without his imagination, which was rampant under the spur of loneliness, he would have succumbed long ago.

Mrs. De Ropp would never, in her honestest moments, have confessed to herself that she disliked Conradin, though she might have been dimly aware that thwarting him "for his good" was a duty which she did not find particularly irksome. Conradin hated her with a desperate sincerity which he was perfectly able to mask. Such few pleasures as he could contrive for himself gained an added relish from the likelihood that they would be displeasing to his guardian, and from the realm of his imagination she was locked out—an unclean thing, which should find no entrance.

In the dull, cheerless garden, overlooked by so many windows that were ready to open with a message not to do this or that, or a reminder that medicines were due, he found little attraction. The few fruit-trees that it contained were set jealously apart from his plucking, as though they were rare specimens of their kind blooming in an arid waste; it would probably have been difficult to find a market-gardener who would have offered ten shillings for their entire yearly produce. In a forgotten corner, however, almost hidden behind a dismal shrubbery, was a disused tool-shed of respectable proportions, and within its walls Conradin found a haven, something that took on the varying aspects of a play-room and a cathedral. He had peopled it with a legion of familiar phantoms,

evoked partly from fragments of history and partly from his own brain,
but it also boasted two inmates of flesh and blood. In one corner lived a
ragged plumaged hen, on which the boy lavished an affection that had
scarcely another outlet. Further back in the gloom stood a large hutch, divided
into two compartments, one of which was fronted with close iron bars. This
was the abode of a large polecat-ferret, which a friendly butcher-boy had once
smuggled, cage and all, into its present quarters, in exchange for a long-secreted
hoard of small silver. Conradin was dreadfully afraid of the lithe, sharp-fanged
beast, but it was his most treasured possession. Its very presence in the tool-shed
was a secret and fearful joy, to be kept scrupulously from the knowledge of the
Woman, as he privately dubbed his cousin. And one day, out of Heaven knows
what material, he spun the beast a wonderful name, and from that moment it
grew into a god and a religion. The Woman indulged in religion once a week at
a church near by, and took Conradin with her, but to him the church service was
an alien rite in the House of Rimmon. Every Thursday, in the dim and musty
silence of the tool-shed, he worshipped with mystic and elaborate ceremonial
before the wooden hutch where dwelt Sredni Vashtar, the great ferret. Red flowers in their season and scarlet berries in the wintertime were offered at his shrine,
for he was a god who laid some special stress on the fierce impatient side of
things, as opposed to the Woman's religion, which, as far as Conradin could
observe, went to great lengths in the contrary direction. And on great festivals
powdered nutmeg was strewn in front of his hutch, an important feature of the
offering being that the nutmeg had to be stolen. These festivals were of irregular
occurrence, and were chiefly appointed to celebrate some passing event. On one
occasion, when Mrs. De Ropp suffered from acute toothache for three days, Conradin kept up the festival during the entire three days, and almost succeeded in
persuading himself that Sredni Vashtar was personally responsible for the toothache. If the malady had lasted for another day the supply of nutmeg would
have given out.

The Houdan hen was never drawn into the cult of Sredni Vashtar. Conradin
had long ago settled that she was an Anabaptist. He did not pretend to have
the remotest knowledge as to what an Anabaptist was, but he privately hoped
that it was dashing and not very respectable. Mrs. De Ropp was the ground plan
on which he based and detested all respectability.

After a while Conradin's absorption in the tool-shed began to attract the
notice of his guardian. "It is not good for him to be pottering down there in all
weathers," she promptly decided, and at breakfast one morning she announced
that the Houdan hen had been sold and taken away overnight. With her short-
sighted eyes she peered at Conradin, waiting for an outbreak of rage and sorrow,
which she was ready to rebuke with a flow of excellent precepts and reasoning.
But Conradin said nothing: there was nothing to be said. Something perhaps in
his white set face gave her a momentary qualm, for at tea that afternoon there
was toast on the table, a delicacy which she usually banned on the ground that
it was bad for him; also because the making of it "gave trouble," a deadly
offence in the middle-class feminine eye.

"I thought you liked toast," she exclaimed, with an injured air, observing that he did not touch it.

"Sometimes," said Conradin.

In the shed that evening there was an innovation in the worship of the hutch-god. Conradin had been wont to chant his praises, tonight he asked a boon.

"Do one thing for me, Sredni Vashtar."

The thing was not specified. As Sredni Vashtar was a god he must be supposed to know. And choking back a sob as he looked at that other empty corner, Conradin went back to the world he so hated.

And every night, in the welcome darkness of his bedroom, and every evening in the dusk of the tool-shed, Conradin's bitter litany went up: "Do one thing for me, Sredni Vashtar."

Mrs. De Ropp noticed that the visits to the shed did not cease, and one day she made a further journey of inspection.

"What are you keeping in that locked hutch?" she asked. "I believe it's guinea-pigs. I'll have them all cleared away."

Conradin shut his lips tight, but the Woman ransacked his bedroom till she found the carefully hidden key, and forthwith marched down to the shed to complete her discovery. It was a cold afternoon, and Conradin had been bidden to keep to the house. From the furthest window of the dining-room the door of the shed could just be seen beyond the corner of the shrubbery, and there Conradin stationed himself. He saw the Woman enter, and then he imagined her opening the door of the sacred hutch and peering down with her short-sighted eyes into the thick straw bed where his god lay hidden. Perhaps she would prod at the straw in her clumsy impatience. And Conradin fervently breathed his prayer for the last time. But he knew as he prayed that he did not believe. He knew that the Woman would come out presently with that pursed smile he loathed so well on her face, and that in an hour or two the gardener would carry away his wonderful god, a god no longer, but a simple brown ferret in a hutch. And he knew that the Woman would triumph always as she triumphed now, and that he would grow ever more sickly under her pestering and domineering and superior wisdom, till one day nothing would matter much more with him, and the doctor would be proved right. And in the sting and misery of his defeat, he began to chant loudly and defiantly the hymn of his threatened idol:

Sredni Vashtar the Beautiful.
His thoughts were red thoughts and his teeth were white.
His enemies called for peace, but he brought them death.
Sredni Vashtar the Beautiful.

And then of a sudden he stopped his chanting and drew closer to the window-pane. The door of the shed still stood ajar as it had been left, and the minutes were slipping by. They were long minutes, but they slipped by nevertheless. He watched the starlings running and flying in little parties across the lawn; he counted them over and over again, with one eye always on that swinging door.

A sour-faced maid came in to lay the table for tea, and still Conradin stood and waited and watched. Hope had crept by inches into his heart, and now a look of triumph began to blaze in his eyes that had only known the wistful patience of defeat. Under his breath, with a furtive exultation, he began once again the paean of victory and devastation. And presently his eyes were rewarded: out through that doorway came a long, low, yellow-and-brown beast, with eyes a-blink at the waning daylight, and dark wet stains around the fur of jaws and throat. Conradin dropped on his knees. The great polecat-ferret made its way down to a small brook at the foot of the garden, drank for a moment, then crossed a little plank bridge and was lost to sight in the bushes. Such was the passing of Sredni Vashtar.

"Tea is ready," said the sour-faced maid; "where is the mistress?"

"She went down to the shed some time ago," said Conradin.

And while the maid went to summon her mistress to tea, Conradin fished a toasting-fork out of the sideboard drawer and proceeded to toast himself a piece of bread. And during the toasting of it and the buttering of it with much butter and the slow enjoyment of eating it, Conradin listened to the noises and silences which fell in quick spasms beyond the dining-room door. The loud foolish screaming of the maid, the answering chorus of wondering ejaculations from the kitchen region, the scuttering footsteps and hurried embassies for outside help, and then, after a lull, the scared sobbings and the shuffling tread of those who bore a heavy burden into the house.

"Whoever will break it to the poor child? I couldn't for the life of me!" exclaimed a shrill voice. And while they debated the matter among themselves, Conradin made himself another piece of toast.

SECTION I

Conradin was ten years old, and the
doctor had pronounced his professional opinion that the boy would
not live another five years. The
doctor was silky and effete, and
counted for little, but his opinion
was endorsed by Mrs. De Ropp,
who counted for nearly everything.
Mrs. De Ropp was Conradin's
cousin and guardian, and in his eyes
she represented those three-fifths of
the world that are necessary and
disagreeable and real; the other two-
fifths, in perpetual antagonism to
the foregoing, were summed up in
himself and his imagination. One of
these days Conradin supposed he
would succumb to the mastering
pressure of wearisome necessary
things—such as illnesses and
coddling restrictions and drawn-out
dulness. Without his imagination,
which was rampant under the spur
of loneliness, he would have succumbed long ago.

   Mrs. De Ropp would never, in her
honestest moments, have confessed
to herself that she disliked Conradin, though she might have been
dimly aware that thwarting him
"for his good" was a duty which
she did not find particularly irksome. Conradin hated her with a
desperate sincerity which he was
perfectly able to mask. Such few
pleasures as he could contrive for
himself gained an added relish from
the likelihood that they would be
displeasing to his guardian, and
from the realm of his imagination
she was locked out—an unclean
thing, which should find no entrance.

SECTION I: QUESTIONS

1
Why does Mrs. De Ropp's opinion about
Conradin's health count more than the
doctor's?

2
Why does Conradin divide the world into
the three-fifths/two-fifths portions? Why
are the divisions not equal?

3
What role does Mrs. De Ropp play in the
"pressure of wearisome necessary things"
and what has so far kept Conradin from
succumbing to them?

4
Is there any suggestion in this section that
Mrs. De Ropp may be in some sense respon-
sible for Conradin's poor health?

5
What are the true feelings of Mrs. De Ropp
and Conradin about each other and how
aware of them is each?

6
In a paragraph or two, define the situation
and Conradin's attitude toward it.

SECTION II

In the dull, cheerless garden, over-looked by so many windows that were ready to open with a message not to do this or that, or a reminder that medicines were due, he found little attraction. The few fruit-trees that it contained were set jealously apart from his plucking, as though they were rare specimens of their kind blooming in an arid waste; it would probably have been difficult to find a market-gardener who would have offered ten shillings for their entire yearly produce. In a for-gotten corner, however, almost hid-den behind a dismal shrubbery, was a disused tool-shed of respectable proportions, and within its walls Conradin found a haven, something that took on the varying aspects of a playroom and a cathedral. He had peopled it with a legion of familiar phantoms, evoked partly from frag-ments of history and partly from his own brain, but it also boasted two inmates of flesh and blood. In one corner lived a ragged plumaged hen, on which the boy lavished an affec-tion that had scarcely another outlet. Further back in the gloom stood a large hutch, divided into two com-partments, one of which was fronted with close iron bars. This was the abode of a large polecat-ferret, which a friendly butcher-boy had once smuggled, cage and all, into its present quarters, in exchange for a long-secreted hoard of small silver. Conradin was dreadfully afraid of the lithe, sharp-fanged beast, but it was his most treasured possession. Its very presence in the tool-shed was a secret and fearful joy, to be kept scrupulously from the knowl-edge of the Woman, as he privately dubbed his cousin. And one day, out of Heaven knows what material he spun the beast a wonderful name, and from that moment it grew into a god and a religion. The Woman indulged in religion once a week at

SECTION II: QUESTIONS

1

What specific details define the garden and the toolshed, making one "dull and cheer-less," and the other an appropriate place for Conradin's playroom?

2

Why does Conradin refer to Mrs. De Ropp as "the Woman"?

3

In what specific ways does Conradin's religion differ from Mrs. De Ropp's? What is suggested about Mrs. De Ropp's religious feelings by saying that she "indulged in religion once a week"?

4

Why is it appropriate that Conradin should worship a creature "who laid special empha-sis on the fierce, impatient side of things," and why is "red" an appropriate color for the flowers and berries he offers at the shrine of his god?

5

How would Conradin define respectability, and why does he hope that the Houdan hen is not respectable?

6

In a paragraph, define the part played by humor in the development of the setting and Conradin's situation.

41

a church near by, and took Conradin
with her, but to him the church service was an alien rite in the House of
Rimmon. Every Thursday, in the
dim and musty silence of the tool-
shed, he worshipped with mystic and
elaborate ceremonial before the
wooden hutch where dwelt Sredni
Vashtar, the great ferret. Red
flowers in their season and scarlet
berries in the wintertime were offered at his shrine, for he was a god
who laid some special stress on the
fierce impatient side of things, as
opposed to the Woman's religion,
which, as far as Conradin could observe, went to great lengths in the
contrary direction. And on great
festivals powdered nutmeg was
strewn in front of his hutch, an
important feature of the offering
being that the nutmeg had to be
stolen. These festivals were of irregular occurrence, and were chiefly
appointed to celebrate some passing
event. On one occasion, when Mrs.
De Ropp suffered from acute toothache for three days, Conradin kept
up the festival during the entire
three days, and almost succeeded in
persuading himself that Sredni
Vashtar was personally responsible
for the toothache. If the malady had
lasted for another day the supply of
nutmeg would have given out.

The Houdan hen was never drawn
into the cult of Sredni Vashtar. Conradin had long ago settled that she
was an Anabaptist. He did not pretend to have the remotest knowledge
as to what an Anabaptist was, but
he privately hoped that it was dashing and not very respectable. Mrs.
De Ropp was the ground plan on
which he based and detested all
respectability.

SECTION III

After a while Conradin's absorption in the tool-shed began to attract the notice of his guardian. "It is not good for him to be pottering down there in all weathers," she promptly decided, and at breakfast one morning she announced that the Houdan hen had been sold and taken away overnight. With her shortsighted eyes she peered at Conradin, waiting for an outbreak of rage and sorrow, which she was ready to rebuke with a flow of excellent precepts and reasoning. But Conradin said nothing: there was nothing to be said. Something perhaps in his white set face gave her a momentary qualm, for at tea that afternoon there was toast on the table, a delicacy which she usually banned on the ground that it was bad for him; also because the making of it "gave trouble," a deadly offence in the middle-class feminine eye.

"I thought you liked toast," she exclaimed, with an injured air, observing that he did not touch it.

"Sometimes," said Conradin.

SECTION III: QUESTIONS

1
What motive does Mrs. De Ropp give for getting rid of the hen? What may be her unstated motive?

2
What is conveyed about Mrs. De Ropp's character by her being "ready to rebuke with a flow of excellent precepts and reasoning"?

3
Why does Conradin accept the loss of his hen with apparent calm?

4
How legitimate are the reasons Conradin is not usually allowed toast at teatime?

5
Why does she offer Conradin toast on this occasion, and why does he refuse it?

6
Discuss in a brief paragraph the details in this section that further reveal the attitudes of these two characters toward each other.

43

SECTION IV

In the shed that evening there was an innovation in the worship of the hutch-god. Conradin had been wont to chant his praises, tonight he asked a boon.

"Do one thing for me, Sredni Vashtar."

The thing was not specified. As Sredni Vashtar was a god he must be supposed to know. And choking back a sob as he looked at that other empty corner, Conradin went back to the world he so hated.

And every night, in the welcome darkness of his bedroom, and every evening in the dusk of the tool-shed, Conradin's bitter litany went up: "Do one thing for me, Sredni Vashtar."

SECTION IV: QUESTIONS

1
Why is it appropriate that Conradin should now ask a special favor from Sredni Vashtar?

2
Why is the prayer a "bitter litany"?

3
If you think there is humor in this section, what does it contribute to your feelings for Conradin?

4
In a paragraph, describe Conradin's feelings at this point and trace their development through the previous sections.

SECTION V

Mrs. De Ropp noticed that the visits to the shed did not cease, and one day she made a further journey of inspection.

"What are you keeping in that locked hutch?" she asked. "I believe it's guinea-pigs. I'll have them all cleared away."

Conradin shut his lips tight, but the Woman ransacked his bedroom till she found the carefully hidden key, and forthwith marched down to the shed to complete her discovery. It was a cold afternoon, and Conradin had been bidden to keep to the house. From the furthest window of the dining-room the door of the shed could just be seen beyond the corner of the shrubbery, and there Conradin stationed himself. He saw the Woman enter, and then he imagined her opening the door of the sacred hutch and peering down with her short-sighted eyes into the thick straw bed where his god lay hidden. Perhaps she would prod at the straw in her clumsy impatience. And Conradin fervently breathed his prayer for the last time. But he knew as he prayed that he did not believe. He knew that the Woman would come out presently with that pursed smile he loathed so well on her face, and that in an hour or two the gardener would carry away his wonderful god, a god no longer, but a simple brown ferret in a hutch. And he knew that the Woman would triumph always as she triumphed now, and that he would grow ever more sickly under her pestering and domineering and superior wisdom, till one day nothing

SECTION V: QUESTIONS

1

What does Mrs. De Ropp's decision to have the shed cleared reveal?

2

What are Conradin's feelings as the Woman ransacks his room for the key to the hutch?

3

How much of the scene does he imagine and how much does he see? What prayer is he breathing "for the last time"?

4

In what sense can the success or failure of Mrs. De Ropp's journey to the toolshed be described as a matter of life or death for Conradin?

5

Why does Conradin begin to chant "loudly and defiantly," and what makes the hymn appropriate for the worship of Sredni Vashtar?

6

In a paragraph, define the dramatic tensions of this section and trace their development.

would matter much more with him, and the doctor would be proved right. And in the sting and misery of his defeat, he began to chant loudly and defiantly the hymn of his threatened idol:

Sredni Vashtar went forth,
His thoughts were red thoughts
and his teeth were white.
His enemies called for peace, but
he brought them death.
Sredni Vashtar the Beautiful.

45

SECTION VI

And then of a sudden he stopped his chanting and drew closer to the window-pane. The door of the shed still stood ajar as it had been left, and the minutes were slipping by. They were long minutes, but they slipped by nevertheless. He watched the starlings running and flying in little parties across the lawn; he counted them over and over again, with one eye always on that swinging door. A sour-faced maid came in to lay the table for tea, and still Conradin stood and waited and watched. Hope had crept by inches into his heart, and now a look of triumph began to blaze in his eyes that had only known the wistful patience of defeat. Under his breath, with a furtive exultation, he began once again the paean of victory and devastation. And presently his eyes were rewarded: out through that doorway came a long, low, yellow-and-brown beast, with eyes a-blink at the waning daylight, and dark wet stains around the fur of jaws and throat. Conradin dropped on his knees. The great polecat-ferret made its way down to a small brook at the foot of the garden, drank for a moment, then crossed a little plank bridge and was lost to sight in the bushes. Such was the passing of Sredni Vashtar.

SECTION VI: QUESTIONS

1
Why does Conradin stop his chanting? What is the dramatic effect of the details which help convey the passage of time as he watches the door of the shed?

2
What is a "paean"? What changes are implied by the "bitter litany" having become a "paean of victory and devastation"?

3
Why is the ferret described as a "long, low, yellow and brown beast" and later as a "great polecat-ferret"? How was the ferret described in the previous section, when Conradin imagined him being removed by the gardener, and what do these contrasts illustrate about Conradin's faith?

4
What are the "dark, wet stains on the fur of the jaw and throat"?

5
What are Conradin's feelings as he watches the ferret leave? What is the significance of the sentence: "Such was the passing of Sredni Vashtar"?

6
In a paragraph show how these details dramatize Conradin's state of mind.

SECTION VII

"Tea is ready," said the sour-faced maid; "where is the mistress?"

"She went down to the shed some time ago," said Conradin.

And while the maid went to summon her mistress to tea, Conradin fished a toasting-fork out of the sideboard drawer and proceeded to toast himself a piece of bread. And during the toasting of it and the buttering of it with much butter and the slow enjoyment of eating it, Conradin listened to the noises and silences which fell in quick spasms beyond the dining-room door. The loud foolish screaming of the maid, the answering chorus of wondering ejaculations from the kitchen region, the scuttering footsteps and hurried embassies for outside help, and then, after a lull, the scared sobbings and the shuffling tread of those who bore a heavy burden into the house.

"Whoever will break it to the poor child? I couldn't for the life of me!" exclaimed a shrill voice. And while they debated the matter among themselves, Conradin made himself another piece of toast.

SECTION VII: QUESTIONS

1

What meanings are compressed into Conradin's actions of fishing out a fork and toasting *himself* a slice of bread, his deliberate movements of "buttering . . . it with much butter" and his "slow enjoyment of eating it"?

2

How does the contrast between the behavior of the servants and the behavior of Conradin dramatize the outcome of the conflict?

3

What has Conradin escaped as a result of the triumph of Sredni Vashtar?

4

What does his action of making "himself another piece of toast" suggest about the present state of his health?

5

Discuss the change in Conradin as revealed in the details of this section.

Sredni Vashtar
Topics for Essays

NOTE. Whichever of these topics you write on and whatever the position you take, remember that your view must rest on an understanding of the details of the story. Your generalizations have to be supported by specific references to the text and by interpretation of those references. Any opinion which is unsupported by evidence is worthless, while any opinion supported by evidence must command respect.

1

Define the vision of life expressed through the story and describe how the sequence, or the character, or the setting, or the situation, or any combination of these elements helps to communicate it.

46

2

Show how the triumph of Conradin and Sredni Vashtar over Mrs. De Ropp could be defined as the triumph of imagination over reality.

3

Examine the relationship of Conradin and Mrs. De Ropp, showing how the nature of this relationship enlists the reader's feelings on the side of Conradin.

4

Discuss the nature of the "cult of Sredni Vashtar," showing the appropriateness of such a religion for a character such as Conradin.

5

Defend or attack the following statement: "The triumph of Conradin and Sredni Vashtar over Mrs. De Ropp is the triumph of the forces of life over the forces of death."

ARABY

JAMES JOYCE

North Richmond Street, being blind, was a quiet street except at the hour when the Christian Brothers' School set the boys free. An uninhabited house of two stories stood at the blind end, detatched from its neighbours in a square ground. The other houses of the street, conscious of decent lives within them, gazed at one another with brown imperturbable faces.

The former tenant of our house, a priest, had died in the back drawing-room. Air, musty from having been long enclosed, hung in all the rooms, and the waste-room behind the kitchen was littered with old useless papers. Among these I found a few paper-covered books, the pages of which were curled and damp: *The Abbot*, by Walter Scott, *The Devout Communicant*, and *The Memoirs of Vidocq*. I liked the last best because its leaves were yellow. The wild garden behind the house contained a central apple tree and a few straggling bushes under one of which I found the late tenant's rusty bicycle pump. He had been a very charitable priest; in his will he had left all his money to institutions and the furniture of his house to his sister.

When the short days of winter came dusk fell before we had well eaten our dinners. When we met in the street the houses had grown sombre. The space of sky above us was the colour of ever-changing violet and towards it the lamps of the street lifted their feeble lanterns. The cold air stung us and we played till our bodies glowed. Our shouts echoed in the silent street. The career of our play brought us through the dark muddy lanes behind the houses where we ran the gauntlet of the rough tribes from the cottages, to the back doors of the dark dripping gardens where odours arose from the ash-pits, to the dark odorous stables where a coachman smoothed and combed the horse or shook music from the buckled harness. When we returned to the street, light from the kitchen windows had filled the areas. If my uncle was seen turning the corner we hid in the shadow until we had seen him safely housed. Or if Mangan's sister came out on the doorstep to call her brother in to his tea we watched her from our

*

From *Dubliners* by James Joyce, originally pub-
lished in 1916 by B. W. Heubsch, Inc. All rights re-
served. Reprinted by permission of The Viking
Press, Inc.

shadow peer up and down the street. We waited to see whether she would remain or go in and, if she remained, we left our shadow and walked up to Mangan's steps resignedly. She was waiting for us, her figure defined by the light from the half-opened door. Her brother always teased her before he obeyed and I stood by the railings looking at her. Her dress swung as she moved her body and the soft rope of her hair tossed from side to side.

Every morning I lay on the floor in the front parlor watching her door. The blind was pulled down to within an inch of the sash so that I could not be seen. When she came out on the doorstep my heart leaped. I ran to the hall, seized my books and followed her. I kept her brown figure always in my eye and, when we came near the point at which our ways diverged, I quickened my pace and passed her. This happened morning after morning. I had never spoken to her, except for a few casual words, and yet her name was like a summons to all my foolish blood.

49

Her image accompanied me even in places the most hostile to romance. On Saturday evenings when my aunt went marketing I had to go to carry some of the parcels. We walked through the flaring streets, jostled by drunken men and bargaining women, amid the curses of labourers, the shrill litanies of shop boys who stood on guard by the barrels of pigs' cheeks, the nasal chanting of street singers, who sang a *come-all-you* about O'Donovan Rossa, or a ballad about the troubles in our native land. These noises converged in a single sensation of life for me: I imagined that I bore my chalice safely through a throng of foes. Her name sprang to my lips at moments in strange prayers and praises which I myself did not understand. My eyes were often full of tears (I could not tell why) and at times a flood from my heart seemed to pour itself out into my bosom. I thought little of the future. I did not know whether I would ever speak to her or not or, if I spoke to her, how I could tell her of my confused adoration. But my body was like a harp and her words and gestures were like fingers running upon the wires.

One evening I went into the back drawing-room in which the priest had died. It was a dark rainy evening and there was no sound in the house. Through one of the broken panes I heard the rain impinge upon the earth, the fine incessant needles of water playing in the sodden beds. Some distant lamp or lighted window gleamed below me. I was thankful that I could see so little. All my senses seemed to desire to veil themselves and, feeling that I was about to slip from them, I pressed the palms of my hands together until they trembled, murmuring: *"O love! O love!"* many times.

At last she spoke to me. When she addressed the first words to me I was so confused that I did not know what to answer. She asked me was I going to *Araby.* I forgot whether I answered yes or no. It would be a splendid bazaar, she said; she would love to go.

"And why can't you?" I asked.

While she spoke she turned a silver bracelet round and round her wrist. She could not go, she said, because there would be a retreat that week in her convent.

Her brother and two other boys were fighting for their caps and I was alone at the railings. She held one of the spikes, bowing her head towards me. The light from the lamp opposite our door caught the white curve of her neck, lit up her hair that rested there and, falling, lit up the hand upon the railing. It fell over one side of her dress and caught the white border of a petticoat, just visible as she stood at ease.

"It's well for you," she said.

"If I go," I said, "I will bring you something."

What innumerable follies laid waste my waking and sleeping thoughts after that evening! I wished to annihilate the tedious intervening days. I chafed against the work of school. At night in my bedroom and by day in the classroom her image came between me and the page I strove to read. The syllables of the word *Araby* were called to me through the silence in which my soul luxuriated and cast an Eastern enchantment over me. I asked for leave to go to the bazaar on Saturday night. My aunt was surprised and hoped it was not some Freemason affair. I answered few questions in class. I watched my master's face pass from amiability to sternness; he hoped I was not beginning to idle. I could not call my wandering thoughts together. I had hardly any patience with the serious work of life which, now that it stood between me and my desire, seemed to me child's play, ugly monotonous child's play.

On Saturday morning I reminded my uncle that I wished to go to the bazaar in the evening. He was fussing at the hall-stand, looking for the hat brush, and answered me curtly:

"Yes, boy, I know."

As he was in the hall I could not go into the front parlour and lie at the window. I left the house in bad humour and walked slowly towards the school. The air was pitilessly raw and already my heart misgave me.

When I came home to dinner my uncle had not yet been home. Still it was early. I sat staring at the clock for some time and, when its ticking began to irritate me, I left the room. I mounted the staircase and gained the upper part of the house. The high cold empty gloomy rooms liberated me and I went from room to room singing. From the front window I saw my companions playing below in the street. Their cries reached me weakened and indistinct and, leaning my forehead against the cool glass, I looked over at the dark house where she lived. I may have stood there for an hour, seeing nothing but the brown-clad figure cast by my imagination, touched discreetly by the lamplight at the curved neck, at the hand upon the railings and at the border below the dress.

When I came downstairs again I found Mrs. Mercer sitting at the fire. She was an old garrulous woman, a pawnbroker's widow, who collected used stamps for some pious purpose. I had to endure the gossip of the tea table. The meal was prolonged beyond an hour and still my uncle did not come. Mrs. Mercer stood up to go: she was sorry she couldn't wait any longer, but it was after eight o'clock and she did not like to be out late, as the night air was bad for her. When she had gone I began to walk up and down the room, clenching my fists. My aunt said:

"I'm afraid you may put off your bazaar for this night of Our Lord."

At nine o'clock I heard my uncle's latchkey in the hall door. I heard him talking to himself and heard the hall-stand rocking when it had received the weight of his overcoat. I could interpret these signs. When he was midway through his dinner I asked him to give me the money to go to the bazaar. He had forgotten.

"The people are in bed and after their first sleep now," he said.

I did not smile. My aunt said to him energetically:

"Can't you give him the money and let him go? You've kept him late enough as it is."

My uncle said he was very sorry he had forgotten. He said he believed in the old saying: "All work and no play makes Jack a dull boy." He asked me where I was going and, when I had told him a second time he asked me did I know *The Arab's Farewell to His Steed*. When I left the kitchen he was about to recite the opening lines of the piece to my aunt.

I held a florin tightly in my hand as I strode down Buckingham Street towards the station. The sight of the streets thronged with buyers and glaring with gas recalled to me the purpose of my journey. I took my seat in a third-class carriage of a deserted train. After an intolerable delay the train moved out of the station slowly. It crept onward among ruinous houses and over the twinkling river. At Westland Row Station a crowd of people pressed to the carriage doors; but the porters moved them back, saying that it was a special train for the bazaar. I remained alone in the bare carriage. In a few minutes the train drew up beside an improvised wooden platform. I passed out on to the road and saw by the lighted dial of a clock that it was ten minutes to ten. In front of me was a large building which displayed the magical name.

I could not find any sixpenny entrance and, fearing that the bazaar would be closed, I passed in quickly through a turnstile, handing a shilling to a weary-looking man. I found myself in a big hall girdled at half its height by a gallery. Nearly all the stalls were closed and the greater part of the hall was in darkness. I recognised a silence like that which pervades a church after a service. I walked into the center of the bazaar timidly. A few people gathered about the stalls which were still open. Before a curtain, over which the words *Café Chantant* were written in coloured lamps, two men were counting money on a salver. I listened to the fall of the coins.

Remembering with difficulty why I had come I went over to one of the stalls and examined porcelain vases and flowered tea-sets. At the door of the stall a young lady was talking and laughing with two young gentlemen. I remarked their English accents and listened vaguely to their conversation.

"O, I never said such a thing!"

"O, but you did!"

"O, but I didn't!"

"Didn't she say that?"

"Yes. I heard her."

"O, there's a . . . fib!"

Observing me, the young lady came over and asked me did I wish to buy any-
· thing. The tone of her voice was not encouraging; she seemed to have spoken
to me out of a sense of duty. I looked humbly at the great jars that stood like
eastern guards at either side of the dark entrance to the stall and murmured:
"No, thank you."

The young lady changed the position of one of the vases and went back to the
two young men. They began to talk of the same subject. Once or twice the young
lady glanced at me over her shoulder.

I lingered before her stall, though I knew my stay was useless, to make my
interest in her wares seem the more real. Then I turned away slowly and walked
down the middle of the bazaar. I allowed the two pennies to fall against the sixpence in my pocket. I heard a voice call from one end of the gallery that the
light was out. The upper part of the hall was now completely dark.

Gazing up into the darkness I saw myself as a creature driven and derided
by vanity; and my eyes burned with anguish and anger.

SECTION I

North Richmond Street, being blind, was a quiet street except at the hour when the Christian Brothers' School set the boys free. An uninhabited house of two stories stood at the blind end, detached from its neighbours in a square ground. The other houses of the street, conscious of decent lives within them, gazed at one another with brown imperturbable faces.

The former tenant of our house, a priest, had died in the back drawing-room. Air, musty from having been long enclosed, hung in all the rooms, and the waste-room behind the kitchen was littered with old useless papers. Among these I found a few paper-covered books, the pages of which were curled and damp: *The Abbot*, by Walter Scott, *The Devout Communicant*, and *The Memoirs of Vidocq*. I liked the last best because its leaves were yellow. The wild garden behind the house contained a central apple tree and a few straggling bushes under one of which I found the late tenant's rusty bicycle pump. He had been a very charitable priest; in his will he had left all his money to institutions and the furniture of his house to his sister.

SECTION II

When the short days of winter came dusk fell before we had well eaten our dinners. When we met in the street the houses had grown sombre. The space of sky above us was the colour of ever-changing violet and towards it the lamps of the street lifted their feeble lanterns. The cold air stung us and we played till our bodies glowed. Our shouts echoed in the silent street. The career of our play brought us through the dark muddy lanes behind the houses where we ran the

SECTION I: QUESTIONS

1
What meanings of the word "blind" are applicable to North Richmond Street?

2
What does the phrase "set the boys free" suggest about the Christian Brothers' School? What does the name of the school in this context suggest about religious institutions?

3
What connection exists between the "decent lives" of the people in the houses, the "brown imperturbable faces" of the houses, and the Christian Brothers' School?

4
What kind of atmosphere is created by the specific details describing the inside of the house? What may be the significance of the former tenant's occupation, the titles of the books he left behind, and the description of the "wild garden" at the back of the house?

5
What common characteristics connect the house to the rest of North Richmond Street?

6
Write a paragraph defining the forces that this setting probably exerts upon the narrator.

SECTION II: QUESTIONS

1
What significance is there in the contrast of light and darkness in this section? Is there any connection between this darkness and the blindness of the previous section?

2
From the narrator's description of Mangan's sister, how would you describe his feelings for her? Has she any relationship to light and darkness?

3
What is suggested by the neighborhood boys' gradual emergence into the light from

53

gauntlet of the rough tribes from the cottages, to the back doors of the dark dripping gardens where odours arose from the ash-pits, to the dark odorous stables where a coachman smoothed and combed the horse or shook music from the buckled harness. When we returned to the street, light from the kitchen windows had filled the areas. If my uncle was seen turning the corner we hid in the shadow until we had seen him safely housed. Or if Mangan's sister came out on the doorstep to call her brother in to his tea we watched her from our shadow peer up and down the street. We waited to see whether she would remain or go in and, if she remained, we left our shadow and walked up to Mangan's steps resignedly. She was waiting for us, her figure defined by the light from the half-opened door. Her brother always teased her before he obeyed and I stood by the railings looking at her. Her dress swung as she moved her body and the soft rope of her hair tossed from side to side.

the anarchy of their play in the dark, dripping, odorous, muddy lanes, gardens and stables? What has the figure of Mangan's sister to do with this emergence?

4
What is added to the setting by references to darkness and light, anarchy and domesticity, freedom and order?

5
Write a paragraph summing up the relationship between the primitive anarchy of the boys' play and the domestic order symbolized by Mangan's sister.

SECTION III

Every morning I lay on the floor in the front parlor watching her door. The blind was pulled down to within an inch of the sash so that I could not be seen. When she came out on the doorstep my heart leaped. I ran to the hall, seized my books and followed her. I kept her brown figure always in my eye and, when we came near the point at which our ways diverged, I quickened my pace and passed her. This happened morning after morning. I had never spoken to her, except for a few casual words, and yet her name was like a summons to all my foolish blood.

SECTION III: QUESTIONS

1
Why doesn't the narrator speak to the girl? In what sense is her name a "summons" to his "foolish" blood? What effect is the girl having upon the narrator?

2
What details about the market place make it "hostile to romance"? What does the use of the word "chalice" in the context say about the narrator's feelings for the girl? How does the metaphor of the harp and harpist define the relationship between the boy and Mangan's sister? Is the boy an active or a passive participant in the relationship?

Her image accompanied me even in places the most hostile to romance. On Saturday evenings when my aunt went marketing I had to go to carry some of the parcels. We walked through the flaring streets, jostled by drunken men and bargaining women, amid the curses of labourers, the shrill litanies of shop boys who stood on guard by the barrels of pigs' cheeks, the nasal chanting of street singers, who sang a *come-all-you* about O'Donovan Rossa, or a ballad about the troubles in our native land. These noises converged in a single sensation of life for me: I imagined that I bore my chalice safely through a throng of foes. Her name sprang to my lips at moments in strange prayers and praises which I myself did not understand. My eyes were often full of tears (I could not tell why) and at times a flood from my heart seemed to pour itself out into my bosom. I thought little of the future. I did not know whether I would ever speak to her or not or, if I spoke to her, how I could tell her of my confused adoration. But my body was like a harp and her words and gestures were like fingers running upon the wires.

One evening I went into the back drawing-room in which the priest had died. It was a dark rainy evening and there was no sound in the house. Through one of the broken panes I heard the rain impinge upon the earth, the fine incessant needles of water playing in the sodden beds. Some distant lamp or lighted window gleamed below me. I was thankful that I could see so little. All my senses seemed to desire to veil themselves and, feeling that I was about to slip from them, I pressed the palms of my hands together until they trembled, murmuring: *"O love! O love!"* many times.

3

How is the situation of the narrator dramatized by the contrast of "litanies," "nasal chanting," "the chalice," "prayers," and "adoration" with the commercial activities of the market place?

4

What aspect of the boy's feeling for Mangan's sister is hinted at by the "needles of water playing in the sodden beds" as the rain "impinges" upon the earth? How comfortable is he about that part of the relationship?

55

5

When he presses his hands together so hard they trembled, what is he praying for and why?

6

Write a paragraph or two defining the boy's situation and the extent to which he is conscious of it. Do not ignore such things as the contrasts of religious terms with commercial activity, darkness with light, freedom with domesticity, and the relationship of Mangan's sister with North Richmond Street and all that it implies. Also, how old is the boy, and how important is his age to his situation?

56

SECTION IV

At last she spoke to me. When she addressed the first words to me I was so confused that I did not know what to answer. She asked me was I going to *Araby*. I forgot whether I answered yes or no. It would be a splendid bazaar, she said; she would love to go.

"And why can't you?" I asked.

While she spoke she turned a silver bracelet round and round her wrist. She could not go, she said, because there would be a retreat that week in her convent. Her brother and two other boys were fighting for their caps and I was alone at the railings. She held one of the spikes, bowing her head towards me. The light from the lamp opposite our door caught the white curve of her neck, lit up her hair that rested there and, falling, lit up the hand upon the railing. It fell over one side of her dress and caught the white border of a petticoat, just visible as she stood at ease.

"It's well for you," she said.

"If I go," I said, "I will bring you something."

SECTION IV: QUESTIONS

1

What aspects of his feelings for Mangan's sister are reinforced by the girl's turning of her silver bracelet while mentioning the "retreat in her convent" and by holding "one of the spikes" while bowing her head toward the boy?

2

What differences between the narrator and his former companions is dramatized here?

3

What is the relationship of the girl to light and darkness in this scene? How much of her is in the light and how much in darkness? How does this image connect to the one in Section II?

4

How does this scene suggest the importance to the boy of his promise to bring the girl something from Araby? What are some of the connotations suggested by the name "Araby," and how do they relate to the boy's feelings about the girl?

5

Write a paragraph defining the narrator's feelings about the girl and the importance of his promise, as established in this section.

SECTION V

What innumerable follies laid waste my waking and sleeping thoughts after that evening! I wished to annihilate the tedious intervening days. I chafed against the work of school. At night in my bedroom and by day in the classroom her image came between me and the page I strove to read. The syllables of the word *Araby* were called to me through the silence in which my soul luxuriated and cast an Eastern enchantment over me. I asked for leave to go to the bazaar on Saturday night. My aunt was surprised and

SECTION V: QUESTIONS

1

What are the "innumerable follies" that dominate the boy's thoughts after his meeting with the girl? In what way are they "follies"?

2

In what way are the "Eastern enchantments" cast by the name of "Araby" related to the boy's feeling about the girl?

3

What cleavage between the boy and his family is dramatized by the difference between his aunt's attitude toward Araby and his own?

hoped it was not some Freemason affair. I answered few questions in class. I watched my master's face pass from amiability to sternness; he hoped I was not beginning to idle. I could not call my wandering thoughts together. I had hardly any patience with the serious work of life which, now that it stood between me and my desire, seemed to me child's play, ugly monotonous child's play.

4
What is the "serious work of life" he has lost patience with, and what does his description of it as "child's play" convey about his present state of mind? What has now become, for the boy, the "serious work of life"?

5
Write a paragraph describing the contrast established in this section between the narrator's previous attitude toward life and his present attitude.

57

SECTION VI

On Saturday morning I reminded my uncle that I wished to go to the bazaar in the evening. He was fussing at the hall-stand, looking for the hat brush, and answered me curtly: "Yes, boy, I know."

As he was in the hall I could not go into the front parlour and lie at the window. I left the house in bad humour and walked slowly towards the school. The air was pitilessly raw and already my heart misgave me.

When I came home to dinner my uncle had not yet been home. Still it was early. I sat staring at the clock for some time and, when its ticking began to irritate me, I left the room. I mounted the staircase and gained the upper part of the house. The high cold empty gloomy rooms liberated me and I went from room to room singing. From the front window I saw my companions playing below in the street. Their cries reached me weakened and indistinct and, leaning my forehead against the cool glass, I looked over at the dark house where she lived. I may have stood there for an hour, seeing nothing but the brown-clad figure cast by my imagination, touched discreetly by the lamplight at the curved neck, at the hand upon the railings and at the border below the dress.

SECTION VI: QUESTIONS

1
What is the uncle's reaction to the boy's reminder that he wants to go to Araby, and how does this reaction dramatize the cleavage between the boy and his family?

2
What kind of atmosphere is suggested by the "high, cold, gloomy rooms" in the upper part of the house? What is it that they "liberate" him from? What does the scene in these rooms illustrate about the change in the relationship between the boy and his former companions?

3
What details about Mrs. Mercer identify her as a typical resident of North Richmond Street, and how do her concerns contrast with the boy's present state of mind?

4
What "signs" does the boy interpret, and what conclusions do they lead the boy to make about his uncle's condition? Is the aunt primarily concerned with the boy, or irritated at her husband? Why does the uncle repeat the old saying? What kind of poem do you think "The Arab's Farewell to His Steed" would be?

5
What is the significance of the fact that the boy, in order to pursue his dream, must depend upon his uncle for money?

When I came downstairs again I found Mrs. Mercer sitting at the fire. She was an old garrulous woman, a pawnbroker's widow, who collected used stamps for some pious purpose. I had to endure the gossip of the tea table. The meal was prolonged beyond an hour and still my uncle did not come. Mrs. Mercer stood up to go: she was sorry she couldn't wait any longer, but it was after eight o'clock and she did not like to be out late, as the night air was bad for her. When she had gone I began to walk up and down the room, clenching my fists. My aunt said:

"I'm afraid you may put off your bazaar for this night of Our Lord."

At nine o'clock I heard my uncle's latchkey in the hall door. I heard him talking to himself and heard the hall-stand rocking when it had received the weight of his overcoat. I could interpret these signs. When he was midway through his dinner I asked him to give me the money to go to the bazaar. He had forgotten.

"The people are in bed and after their first sleep now," he said.

I did not smile. My aunt said to him energetically:

"Can't you give him the money and let him go? You've kept him late enough as it is."

My uncle said he was very sorry he had forgotten. He said he believed in the old saying: "All work and no play makes Jack a dull boy." He asked me where I was going and, when I had told him a second time he asked me did I know *The Arab's Farewell to His Steed*. When I left the kitchen he was about to recite the opening lines of the piece to my aunt.

58

6
Write a paragraph or two exploring the tensions and connections between the setting of adult North Richmond Street and the boy's situation.

SECTION VII

I held a florin tightly in my hand as I strode down Buckingham Street towards the station. The sight of the streets thronged with buyers and glaring with gas recalled to me the purpose of my journey. I took my seat in a third-class carriage of a deserted train. After an intolerable delay the train moved out of the station slowly. It crept onward among ruinous houses and over the twinkling river. At Westland Row Station a crowd of people pressed to the carriage doors; but the porters moved them back, saying that it was a special train for the bazaar. I re-mained alone in the bare carriage. In a few minutes the train drew up beside an improvised wooden plat-form. I passed out on to the road and saw by the lighted dial of a clock that it was ten minutes to ten. In front of me was a large building which displayed the magical name.

SECTION VII: QUESTIONS

1

How does this description of the streets define the literal purpose of the boy's journey?

2

What does the slowness of the train empha-size about the boy's state of mind?

3

What idea is suggested by the boy's isola-tion in an empty carriage on a "special" train?

4

Write a paragraph showing how the details of this section build up the contrast between the boy's state of mind and the real world. How is this contrast related to his feelings about Mangan's sister?

SECTION VIII

I could not find any sixpenny entrance and, fearing that the bazaar
would be closed, I passed in quickly
through a turnstile, handing a shilling to a weary-looking man. I found
myself in a big hall girdled at half
its height by a gallery. Nearly all the
stalls were closed and the greater
part of the hall was in darkness. I
recognized a silence like that which
pervades a church after a service. I
walked into the center of the bazaar
timidly. A few people were gathered
about the stalls which were still
open. Before a curtain, over which
the words *Café Chantant* were written in coloured lamps, two men were
counting money on a salver. I listened to the fall of the coins.

Remembering with difficulty why
I had come I went over to one of the
stalls and examined porcelain vases
and flowered tea-sets. At the door of
the stall a young lady was talking
and laughing with two young gentlemen. I remarked their English accents and listened vaguely to their
conversation.

"O, I never said such a thing!"

"O, but you did!"

"O, but I didn't!"

"Didn't she say that?"

"Yes. I heard her."

"O, there's a . . . fib!"

Observing me, the young lady
came over and asked me did I wish
to buy anything. The tone of her
voice was not encouraging; she
seemed to have spoken to me out of
a sense of duty. I looked humbly at
the great jars that stood like eastern
guards at either side of the dark entrance to the stall and murmured:

"No, thank you."

The young lady changed the position of one of the vases and went
back to the two young men. They
began to talk of the same subject.
Once or twice the young lady
glanced at me over her shoulder.

SECTION VIII: QUESTIONS

1

What is suggested by the frequent references to money in the first paragraph of this
section and how are they related to religion,
romance, light and darkness, and the indifferent world? What image of Araby do these
details build?

2

Why does the impact of Araby as it really is
cause the boy momentarily to forget the
specific purpose of his journey?

3

Judging from their conversation, what are
the two young men interested in?
What is the connection between the interest
of the young gentlemen and the interest
which brought the boy to Araby?

4

Write a paragraph showing the relationship
between the boy's decision not to buy anything and the details in the description of
"Araby," including the scene between the
shop girl and the gentlemen.

SECTION IX

I lingered before her stall, though I knew my stay was useless, to make my interest in her wares seem the more real. Then I turned away slowly and walked down the middle of the bazaar. I allowed the two pennies to fall against the sixpence in my pocket. I heard a voice call from one end of the gallery that the light was out. The upper part of the hall was now completely dark.

Gazing up into the darkness I saw myself as a creature driven and derided by vanity; and my eyes burned with anguish and anger.

SECTION IX: QUESTIONS

1

In what double sense is the boy's lack of interest in the young lady's "wares" connected with his refusal to buy in the preceding section and his relationship with Mangan's sister?

2

Why is the boy now playing with his money?

3

What other lights may have gone out along with the lights in the upper part of the hall?

4

Why does the boy see himself as a "creature" as he gazes up into the darkness? How has he formerly thought of himself?

5

In what sense has the boy been "driven and derided by vanity"? Why does this realization makes his eyes burn with anguish? Why does it make them burn with anger? Does the fact that he feels these emotions simultaneously suggest anything about ambiguity of human feelings?

6

Write a paragraph showing the relationship of the details in the first paragraph of this section to the boy's realization in the final line of the story.

61

Araby
Topics for Essays

NOTE. Whichever of these topics you write on and whatever the position you take, remember that your view must rest on an understanding of the details of the story. Your generalizations have to be supported by specific references to the text and by interpretation of those references. Any opinion which is unsupported by evidence is worthless, while any opinion supported by evidence must command respect.

1

Define the vision of life expressed through the story and describe how the sequence, or the character, or the setting, or the situation, or any combination of these elements helps to communicate it.

2

Define the nature of the personal crisis the boy in "Araby" is undergoing, and trace its stages through the sequence of sections.

3

What is the relationship between the title and the complex experience of the boy?

4

Defend or attack the following statement: "The boy's new awareness at the end of the story, though terrible, will save him from the tragedy of North Richmond Street."

NATHANIEL HAWTHORNE   YOUNG GOODMAN BROWN

Young Goodman Brown came forth at sunset into the street at Salem village;
but put his head back, after crossing the threshold, to exchange a parting kiss
with his young wife. And Faith, as the wife was aptly named, thrust her own
pretty head into the street, letting the wind play with the pink ribbons of her cap
while she called to Goodman Brown.

"Dearest heart," whispered she, softly and rather sadly, when her lips were
close to his ear, "prithee put off your journey until sunrise and sleep in
your own bed to-night. A lone woman is troubled with such dreams and such
thoughts that she's afeard of herself sometimes. Pray tarry with me this night,
dear husband, of all nights in the year."

"My love and my Faith," replied young Goodman Brown, "of all nights in the
year, this one night must I tarry away from thee. My journey, as thou callest it,
forth and back again, must needs be done 'twixt now and sunrise. What, my
sweet, pretty wife, dost thou doubt me already, and we but three months married?"

"Then God bless you!" said Faith, with the pink ribbons; "and may you find
all well when you come back."

"Amen!" cried Goodman Brown. "Say thy prayers, dear Faith, and go to bed
at dusk, and no harm will come to thee."

So they parted; and the young man pursued his way until, being about to
turn the corner by the meeting-house, he looked back and saw the head of Faith
still peeping after him with a melancholy air, in spite of her pink ribbons.

"Poor little Faith!" thought he, for his heart smote him. "What a wretch am I to
leave her on such an errand! She talks of dreams too. Methought as she spoke
there was trouble in her face, as if a dream had warned her what work is to be
done to-night. But no, no; 'twould kill her to think it. Well, she's a blessed
angel on earth; and after this one night I'll cling to her skirts and follow her
to heaven."

With this excellent resolve for the future, Goodman Brown felt himself justified in making more haste on his present evil purpose. He had taken a dreary
road, darkened by all the gloomiest trees of the forest, which barely stood aside
to let the narrow path creep through, and closed immediately behind. It was all
as lonely as could be; and there is this peculiarity in such a solitude, that the
traveller knows not who may be concealed by the innumerable trunks and the

thick boughs overhead; so that with lonely footsteps he may yet be passing through an unseen multitude.

"There may be a devilish Indian behind every tree," said Goodman Brown to himself; and he glanced fearfully behind him as he added, "What if the devil himself should be at my very elbow!"

His head being turned back, he passed a crook of the road, and, looking forward again, beheld the figure of a man, in grave and decent attire, seated at the foot of an old tree. He arose at Goodman Brown's approach and walked onward side by side with him.

"You are late, Goodman Brown," said he. "The clock of the Old South was striking as I came through Boston, and that is full fifteen minutes agone."

"Faith kept me back a while," replied the young man, with a tremor in his voice, caused by the sudden appearance of his companion, though not wholly unexpected.

It was now deep dusk in the forest, and deepest in that of it where these two were journeying. As nearly as could be discerned, the second traveller was about fifty years old, apparently in the same rank of life as Goodman Brown, and bearing a considerable resemblance to him, though perhaps more in expression than features. Still they might have been taken for father and son. And yet, though the elder person was as simply clad as the younger, and as simple in manner too, he had an indescribable air of one who knew the world, and who would not have felt abashed at the governor's dinner table or in King William's court, were it possible that his affairs should call him thither. But the only thing about him that could be fixed upon as remarkable was his staff, which bore the likeness of a great black snake, so curiously wrought that it might almost be seen to twist and wriggle itself like a living serpent. This, of course, must have been an ocular deception, assisted by the uncertain light.

"Come, Goodman Brown," cried his fellow-traveller, "this is a dull pace for the beginning of a journey. Take my staff, if you are so soon weary."

"Friend," said the other, exchanging his slow pace for a full stop, "having kept covenant by meeting thee here, it is my purpose now to return whence I came. I have scruples touching the matter thou wot'st of."

"Sayest thou so?" replied he of the serpent, smiling apart. "Let us walk on, nevertheless, reasoning as we go; and if I convince thee not thou shalt turn back. We are but a little way in the forest yet."

"Too far! too far!" exclaimed the goodman, unconsciously resuming his walk. "My father never went into the woods on such an errand, nor his father before him. We have been a race of honest men and good Christians since the days of the martyrs; and shall I be the first of the name of Brown that ever took his path and kept"—

"Such company, thou wouldst say," observed the elder person, interpreting his pause. "Well said, Goodman Brown! I have been as well acquainted with your family as with ever a one among the Puritans; and that's no trifle to say. I helped your grandfather, the constable, when he lashed the Quaker woman so smartly through the streets of Salem; and it was I that brought your father a pitch-pine knot, kindled at my own hearth, to set fire to an Indian village, in King Philip's war. They were my good friends, both; and many a pleasant walk have we had along this path, and returned merrily after midnight. I would fain be friends with you for their sake."

"If it be as thou sayest," replied Goodman Brown, "I marvel they never spoke of these matters; or verily, I marvel not, seeing the least rumor of the sort would have driven them from New England. We are a people of prayer, and good works to boot, and abide no such wickedness."

"Wickedness or not," said the traveller with the twisted staff, "I have a very general acquaintance here in New England. The deacons of many a church have drunk the communion wine with me; the selectmen of divers towns make me their chairman; and a majority of the Great and General Court are firm supporters of my interest. The governor and I, too—But these are state secrets."

"Can this be so?" cried Goodman Brown, with a stare of amazement at his undisturbed companion. "Howbeit, I have nothing to do with the governor and council; they have their own ways, and are no rule for a simple husbandman like me. But, were I to go on with thee, how should I meet the eye of that good old man, our minister, at Salem village? Oh, his voice would make me tremble both Sabbath day and lecture day."

Thus far the elder traveller had listened with due gravity; but now burst into a fit of irrepressible mirth, shaking himself so violently that his snake-like staff actually seemed to wriggle in sympathy.

"Ha! ha! ha!" shouted he again and again; then composing himself, "Well, go on, Goodman Brown, go on; but, prithee, don't kill me with laughing."

"Well, then, to end the matter at once," said Goodman Brown, considerably nettled, "there is my wife, Faith. It would break her dear little heart; and I'd rather break my own."

"Nay, if that be the case," answered the other, "e'en go thy ways, Goodman Brown. I would not for twenty old women like the one hobbling before us that Faith should come to any harm."

As he spoke he pointed his staff at a female figure on the path, in whom Goodman Brown recognized a very pious and exemplary dame, who had taught him his catechism in youth, and was still his moral and spiritual adviser, jointly with the minister and Deacon Gookin.

"A marvel, truly, that Goody Cloyse should be so far in the wilderness at nightfall," said he. "But with your leave, friend, I shall take a cut through the woods until we have left this Christian woman behind. Being a stranger to you, she might ask whom I was consorting with and whither I was going."

"Be it so," said his fellow-traveller. "Betake you to the woods, and let me keep the path."

Accordingly the young man turned aside, but took care to watch his companion, who advanced softly along the road until he had come within a staff's length of the old dame. She, meanwhile, was making the best of her way, with

65

singular speed for so aged a woman, and mumbling some indistinct words—a prayer, doubtless—as she went. The traveller put forth his staff and touched her withered neck with what seemed the serpent's tail.

"The devil!" screamed the pious old lady.

"Then Goody Cloyse knows her old friend?" observed the traveller, confronting her and leaning on his writhing stick.

"Ah, forsooth, and is it your worship indeed?" cried the good dame. "Yea, truly is it, and in the very image of my old gossip, Goodman Brown, the grandfather of the silly fellow that now is. But—would your worship believe it?—my broomstick hath strangely disappeared, stolen, as I suspect, by that unhanged witch, Goody Cory, and that, too, when I was all anointed with the juice of smallage, and cinquefoil, and wolf's bane"—

"Mingled with fine wheat and the fat of a new-born babe," said the shape of old Goodman Brown.

"Ah, your worship knows the recipe," cried the old lady, cackling aloud. "So, as I was saying, being all ready for the meeting, and no horse to ride on, I made up my mind to foot it; for they tell me there is a nice young man to be taken into communion tonight. But now your good worship will lend me your arm, and we shall be there in a twinkling."

"That can hardly be," answered her friend. "I may not spare you my arm, Goody Cloyse; but here is my staff, if you will."

So saying, he threw it down at her feet, where, perhaps, it assumed life, being one of the rods which its owner had formerly lent to the Egyptian magi. Of this fact, however, Goodman Brown could not take cognizance. He had cast up his eyes in astonishment, and, looking down again, beheld neither Goody Cloyse nor the serpentine staff, but his fellow-traveller alone, who waited for him as calmly as if nothing had happened.

"That old woman taught me my catechism," said the young man; and there was a world of meaning in this simple comment.

They continued to walk onward, while the elder traveller exhorted his companion to make good speed and persevere in the path, discoursing so aptly that his arguments seemed rather to spring up in the bosom of his auditor than to be suggested by himself. As they went, he plucked a branch of maple to serve for a walking stick, and began to strip it of the twigs and little boughs, which were wet with evening dew. The moment his fingers touched them they became strangely withered and dried up as with a week's sunshine. Thus the pair proceeded, at a good free pace, until suddenly, in a gloomy hollow of the road, Goodman Brown sat himself down on the stump of a tree and refused to go any farther.

"Friend," said he, stubbornly, "my mind is made up. Not another step will I budge on this errand. What if a wretched old woman do choose to go to the devil when I thought she was going to heaven: is that any reason why I should quit my dear Faith and go after her?"

"You will think better of this by and by," said his acquaintance, composedly.

"Sit here and rest yourself a while; and when you feel like moving again, there
is my staff to help you along."

Without more words, he threw his companion the maple stick, and was as
speedily out of sight as if he had vanished into the deepening gloom. The young
man sat a few moments by the roadside, applauding himself greatly, and thinking with how clear a conscience he should meet the minister in his morning
walk, nor shrink from the eye of good old Deacon Gookin. And what calm sleep
would be his that very night, which was to have been spent so wickedly, but so
purely and sweetly now, in the arms of Faith! Amidst these pleasant and praise-
worthy meditations, Goodman Brown heard the tramp of horses along the road,
and deemed it advisable to conceal himself within the verge of the forest, conscious of the guilty purpose that had brought him thither, though now so happily
turned from it.

67

On came the hoof tramps and the voices of the riders, two grave old voices,
conversing soberly as they drew near. These mingled sounds appeared to pass
along the road, within a few yards of the young man's hiding-place; but, owing
doubtless to the depth of the gloom at that particular spot, neither the travellers
nor their steeds were visible. Though their figures brushed the small boughs
by the wayside, it could not be seen that they intercepted, even for a moment,
the faint gleam from the strip of bright sky athwart which they must have
passed. Goodman Brown alternately crouched and stood on tiptoe, pulling aside
the branches and thrusting forth his head as far as he durst without discerning
so much as a shadow. It vexed him the more, because he could have sworn, were
such a thing possible, that he recognized the voices of the minister and Deacon
Gookin, jogging along quietly, as they were wont to do, when bound to some
ordination or ecclesiastical council. While yet within hearing, one of the riders
stopped to pluck a switch.

"Of the two, reverend sir," said the voice like the deacon's, "I had rather miss
an ordination dinner than to-night's meeting. They tell me that some of our
community are to be here from Falmouth and beyond and others from Connecticut and Rhode Island, besides several of Indian powwows, who, after their
fashion, know almost as much deviltry as the best of us. Moreover, there is a
goodly young woman to be taken into communion."

"Mighty well, Deacon Gookin!" replied the solemn old tones of the minister.
"Spur up, or we shall be late. Nothing can be done, you know, until I get on the
ground."

The hoofs clattered again; and the voices, talking so strangely in the empty
air, passed on through the forest, where no church had ever been gathered or
solitary Christian prayed. Whither, then, could these holy men be journeying so
deep into the heathen wilderness? Young Goodman Brown caught hold of a tree
for support, being ready to sink down on the ground, faint and overburdened
with the heavy sickness of his heart. He looked up to the sky, doubting whether
there really was a heaven above him. Yet there was the blue arch, and the stars
brightening in it.

"With heaven above and Faith below, I will yet stand firm against the devil!" cried Goodman Brown.

While he still gazed upward into the deep arch of the firmament and had lifted his hands to pray, a cloud, though no wind was stirring, hurried across the zenith and hid the brightening stars. The blue sky was still visible, except directly overhead, where this black mass of cloud was sweeping swiftly northward. Aloft in the air, as if from the depths of the cloud, came a confused and doubtful sound of voices. Once the listener fancied that he could distinguish the accents of towns-people of his own, men, and women, both pious and ungodly, many of whom he had met at the communion table, and had seen others rioting at the tavern. The next moment, so indistinct were the sounds, he doubted whether he had heard aught but the murmur of the old forest, whispering without a wind. Then came a stronger swell of those familiar tones, heard daily in the sunshine at Salem village, but never until now from a cloud of night. There was one voice of a young woman, uttering lamentations, yet with an uncertain sorrow, and entreating for some favor, which, perhaps, it would grieve her to obtain; and all the unseen multitude, both saints and sinners, seemed to encourage her onward.

"Faith!" shouted Goodman Brown, in a voice of agony and desperation; and the echoes of the forest mocked him, crying, "Faith! Faith!" as if bewildered wretches were seeking her all through the wilderness.

The cry of grief, rage, and terror was yet piercing the night, when the unhappy husband held his breath for a response. There was a scream, drowned immediately in a louder murmur of voices, fading into far-off laughter, as the dark cloud swept away, leaving the clear and silent sky above Goodman Brown. But something fluttered lightly down through the air and caught on the branch of a tree. The young man seized it, and beheld a pink ribbon.

"My Faith is gone!" cried he, after one stupefied moment. "There is no good on earth; and sin is but a name. Come, devil; for to thee is this world given."

And, maddened with despair, so that he laughed loud and long, did Goodman Brown grasp his staff and set forth again, at such a rate that he seemed to fly along the forest path rather than to walk or run. The road grew wilder and drearier and more faintly traced, and vanished at length, leaving him in the heart of the dark wilderness, still rushing onward with the instinct that guides mortal man to evil. The whole forest was peopled with frightful sounds—the creaking of the trees, the howling of wild beasts, and the yell of Indians; while sometimes the wind tolled like a distant church bell, and sometimes gave a broad roar around the traveller, as if all Nature were laughing him to scorn. But he was himself the chief horror of the scene, and shrank not from its other horrors.

"Ha! ha! ha!" roared Goodman Brown when the wind laughed at him. "Let us hear which will laugh loudest. Think not to frighten me with your deviltry. Come witch, come wizard, come Indian powwow, come devil himself, and here comes Goodman Brown. You may as well fear him as he fear you."

In truth, all through the haunted forest there could be nothing more frightful than the figure of Goodman Brown. On he flew among the black pines, brandishing his staff with frenzied gestures, now giving vent to an inspiration of horrid blasphemy, and now shouting forth such laughter as set all the echoes of the forest laughing like demons around him. The fiend in his own shape is less hideous than when he rages in the breast of man. Thus sped the demoniac on his course, until, quivering among the trees, he saw a red light before him, as when the felled trunks and branches of a clearing have been set on fire, and throw up their lurid blaze against the sky, at the hour of midnight. He paused, in a lull of the tempest that had driven him onward, and heard the swell of what seemed a hymn, rolling solemnly from a distance with the weight of many voices. He knew the tune; it was a familiar one in the choir of the village meeting house. The verse died heavily away, and was lengthened by a chorus, not of human voices, but of all the sounds of the benighted wilderness pealing in awful harmony together. Goodman Brown cried out, and his cry was lost to his own ear by its unison with the cry of the desert.

In the interval of silence he stole forward until the light glared full upon his eyes. At one extremity of an open space, hemmed in by the dark wall of the forest, arose a rock, bearing some rude, natural resemblance either to an altar or a pulpit, and surrounded by four blazing pines, their tops aflame, their stems untouched, like candles at an evening meeting. The mass of foliage that had overgrown the summit of the rock was all on fire, blazing high into the night and fitfully illuminating the whole field. Each pendent twig and leafy festoon was in a blaze. As the red light arose and fell, a numerous congregation alternately shone forth, then disappeared in shadow, and again grew, as it were, out of the darkness, peopling the heart of the solitary woods at once.

"A grave and dark-clad company," quoth Goodman Brown.

In truth they were such. Among them, quivering to and fro between gloom and splendor, appeared faces that would be seen next day at the council board of the province, and others which, Sabbath after Sabbath, looked devoutly heavenward, and benignantly over the crowded pews, from the holiest pulpits in the land. Some affirm that the lady of the governor was there. At least there were high dames well known to her, and wives of honored husbands, and widows, a great multitude, and ancient maidens, all of excellent repute, and fair young girls, who trembled lest their mothers should espy them. Either the sudden gleams of light flashing over the obscure field bedazzled Goodman Brown, or he recognized a score of the church members of Salem village famous for their especial sanctity. Good old Deacon Gookin had arrived, and waited at the skirts of that venerable saint, his revered pastor. But, irreverently consorting with these grave, reputable, and pious people, these elders of the church, these chaste dames and dewy virgins, there were men of dissolute lives and women of spotted fame, wretches given over to all mean and filthy vice, and suspected even of horrid crimes. It was strange to see that the good shrank not from the wicked, nor were the sinners abashed by the saints. Scattered also among their pale-faced enemies were the Indian priests, or powwows, who had often scared their native forest with more hideous incantations than any known to English witchcraft.

"But where is Faith?" thought Goodman Brown; and, as hope came into his heart, he trembled.

Another verse of the hymn arose, a slow and mournful strain, such as the pious love, but joined to words which expressed all that our nature can conceive of sin, and darkly hinted at far more. Unfathomable to mere mortals is the lore of fiends. Verse after verse was sung; and still the chorus of the desert swelled between like the deepest tone of a mighty organ; and with the final peal of that dreadful anthem there came a sound, as if the roaring wind, the rushing streams, the howling beasts, and every other voice of the unconcerted wilderness were mingling and according with the voice of guilty man in homage to the prince of all. The four blazing pines threw up a loftier flame, and obscurely discovered shapes and visages of horror on the smoke wreaths above the impious assembly. At the same moment the fire on the rock shot redly forth and formed a glowing arch above its base, where now appeared a figure. With reverence be it spoken, the figure bore no slight similitude, both in garb and manner, to some grave divine of the New England churches.

"Bring forth the converts!" cried a voice that echoed through the field and rolled into the forest.

At the word, Goodman Brown stepped forth from the shadow of the trees and approached the congregation, with whom he felt a loathful brotherhood by the sympathy of all that was wicked in his heart. He could have well-nigh sworn that the shape of his own dead father beckoned him to advance, looking downward from a smoke wreath, while a woman, with dim features of despair, threw out her hand to warn him back. Was it his mother? But he had no power to retreat one step, nor to resist, even in thought, when the minister and good old Deacon Gookin seized his arms and led him to the blazing rock. Thither came also the slender form of a veiled female, led between Goody Cloyse, that pious teacher of the catechism, and Martha Carrier, who had received the devil's promise to be queen of hell. A rampant hag was she. And there stood the proselytes beneath the canopy of fire.

"Welcome, my children," said the dark figure, "to the communion of your race. Ye have found thus young your nature and your destiny. My children, look behind you!"

They turned; and flashing forth, as it were, in a sheet of flame, the fiend worshippers were seen; the smile of welcome gleamed darkly on every visage.

"There," resumed the sable form, "are all whom ye have reverenced from youth. Ye deemed them holier than yourselves, and shrank from your own sin, contrasting it with their lives of righteousness and prayerful aspirations heavenward. Yet here are they all in my worshipping assembly. This night it shall be granted you to know their secret deeds: how hoary-bearded elders of the church have whispered wanton words to the young maids of their households; how many a woman, eager for widows' weeds, has given her husband a drink at bedtime and let him sleep his last sleep in her bosom; how beardless youths have made haste to inherit their fathers' wealth; and how fair damsels—blush not, sweet ones —have dug little graves in the garden, and bidden me, the sole guest to an infant's funeral. By the sympathy of your human hearts for sin ye shall scent out all the places—whether in church, bedchamber, street, field, or forest—where crime has been committed, and shall exult to behold the whole earth one stain of guilt, one mighty blood spot. Far more than this. It shall be yours to penetrate, in every bosom, the deep mystery of sin, the fountain of all wicked arts, which inexhaustibly supplies more evil impulses than human power—than my power at its utmost—can make manifest in deeds. And now, my children, look upon each other."

71

They did so; and, by the blaze of the hell-kindled torches, the wretched man beheld his Faith, and the wife her husband, trembling before that unhallowed altar.

"Lo, there ye stand, my children," said the figure, in a deep and solemn tone, almost sad with its despairing awfulness, as if his once angelic nature could yet mourn for our miserable race. "Depending upon one another's hearts, ye had still hoped that virtue were not all a dream. Now are ye undeceived. Evil is the nature of mankind. Evil must be your only happiness. Welcome again, my children, to the communion of your race."

"Welcome," repeated the fiend worshippers, in one cry of despair and triumph.

And there they stood, the only pair, as it seemed, who were yet hesitating on the verge of wickedness in this dark world. A basin was hollowed, naturally, in the rock. Did it contain water, reddened by the lurid light? or was it blood? or, perchance, a liquid flame? Herein did the shape of evil dip his hand and prepare to lay the mark of baptism upon their foreheads, that they might be partakers of the mystery of sin, more conscious of the secret guilt of others, both in deed and thought, than they could now be of their own. The husband cast one look at his pale wife, and Faith at him. What polluted wretches would the next glance show them to each other, shuddering alike at what they disclosed and what they saw!

"Faith! Faith!" cried the husband, "look up to heaven, and resist the wicked one."

Whether Faith obeyed he knew not. Hardly had he spoken when he found himself amid calm night and solitude, listening to a roar of the wind which died heavily away through the forest. He staggered against the rock, and felt it chill and damp; while a hanging twig, that had been all on fire, besprinkled his cheek with the coldest dew.

The next morning young Goodman Brown came slowly into the street of Salem village, staring around him like a bewildered man. The good old minister was taking a walk along the graveyard to get an appetite for breakfast and meditate his sermon, and bestowed a blessing, as he passed, on Goodman Brown. He shrank from the venerable saint as if to avoid an anathema. Old Deacon

Gookin was at domestic worship, and the holy words of his prayer were heard through the open window. "What God doth the wizard pray to?" quoth Goodman Brown. Goody Cloyse, that excellent old Christian, stood in the early sunshine at her own lattice, catechizing a little girl who had brought her a pint of morning's milk. Goodman Brown snatched away the child as from the grasp of the fiend himself. Turning the corner by the meeting-house, he spied the head of Faith, with the pink ribbons, gazing anxiously forth, and bursting into such joy at sight of him that she skipped along the street and almost kissed her husband before the whole village. But Goodman Brown looked sternly and sadly into her face, and passed on without a greeting.

Had Goodman Brown fallen asleep in the forest and only dreamed a wild dream of a witch-meeting?

Be it so if you will; but, alas! it was a dream of evil omen for young Goodman Brown. A stern, a sad, a darkly meditative, a distrustful, if not a desperate man did he become from the night of that fearful dream. On the Sabbath day, when the congregation were singing a holy psalm, he could not listen because an anthem of sin rushed loudly upon his ear and drowned all the blessed strain. When the minister spoke from the pulpit with power and fervid eloquence, and, with his hand on the open Bible, of the sacred truths of our religion, and of saint-like lives and triumphant deaths, and of future bliss or misery unutterable, then did Goodman Brown turn pale, dreading lest the roof should thunder down upon the gray blasphemer and his hearers. Often, waking suddenly at midnight, he shrank from the bosom of Faith; and at morning or eventide, when the family knelt down at prayer, he scowled and muttered to himself, and gazed sternly at his wife, and turned away. And when he lived long, and was borne to his grave a hoary corpse, followed by Faith, an aged woman, and children and grandchildren, a goodly procession, besides neighbors not a few, they carved no hopeful verse upon his tombstone, for his dying hour was gloom.

72

SECTION I

Young Goodman Brown came forth at sunset into the street at Salem village; but put his head back, after crossing the threshold, to exchange a parting kiss with his young wife. And Faith, as the wife was aptly named, thrust her own pretty head into the street, letting the wind play with the pink ribbons of her cap while she called to Goodman Brown. "Dearest heart," whispered she, softly and rather sadly, when her lips were close to his ear, "prithee put off your journey until sunrise

SECTION I: QUESTIONS

1

What is suggested by the names of the man and his wife? What details in the description of the wife define some of the meanings of the term "faith"? In what sense is the wife "aptly named"?

2

How do you know the kind of journey that Goodman Brown is setting out upon?

3

What are the tensions between Goodman Brown and Faith and how are they illustrated through physical descriptions?

and sleep in your own bed to-night.
A lone woman is troubled with such
dreams and such thoughts that she's
afeard of herself sometimes. Pray
tarry with me this night, dear husband, of all nights in the year."

"My love and my Faith," replied
young Goodman Brown, "of all
nights in the year, this one night
must I tarry away from thee. My
journey, as thou callest it, forth and
back again, must needs be done
'twixt now and sunrise. What, my
sweet, pretty wife, dost thou doubt
me already, and we but three
months married?"

"Then God bless you!" said Faith,
with the pink ribbons; "and may
you find all well when you come
back."

"Amen!" cried Goodman Brown.
"Say thy prayers, dear Faith, and
go to bed at dusk, and no harm will
come to thee"

So they parted; and the young
man pursued his way until, being
about to turn the corner by the
meeting-house, he looked back and
saw the head of Faith still peeping
after him with a melancholy air, in
spite of her pink ribbons.

"Poor little Faith!" thought he, for
his heart smote him. "What a
wretch am I to leave her on such
an errand! She talks of dreams too.
Methought as she spoke there was
trouble in her face, as if a dream had
warned her what work is to be done
to-night. But no, no; 'twould kill her
to think it. Well, she's a blessed
angel on earth; and after this one
night I'll cling to her skirts and follow her to heaven."

4

In a paragraph define the relationship between Goodman Brown and Faith, the tensions on the ideological level which it
suggests, and the atmosphere in which they
combine and develop.

73

SECTION II

74

With this excellent resolve for the future, Goodman Brown felt himself justified in making more haste on his present evil purpose. He had taken a dreary road, darkened by all the gloomiest trees of the forest, which barely stood aside to let the narrow path creep through, and closed immediately behind. It was all as lonely as could be; and there is this peculiarity in such a solitude, that the traveller knows not who may be concealed by the innumerable trunks and the thick boughs overhead; so that with lonely footsteps he may yet be passing through an unseen multitude.

"There may be a devilish Indian behind every tree," said Goodman Brown to himself; and he glanced fearfully behind him as he added, "What if the devil himself should be at my very elbow!"

His head being turned back, he passed a crook of the road, and, looking forward again, beheld the figure of a man, in grave and decent attire, seated at the foot of an old tree. He arose at Goodman Brown's approach and walked onward side by side with him.

"You are late, Goodman Brown," said he. "The clock of the Old South was striking as I came through Boston, and that is full fifteen minutes agone."

"Faith kept me back a while," replied the young man, with a tremor in his voice, caused by the sudden appearance of his companion, though not wholly unexpected.

It was now deep dusk in the forest, and deepest in that part of it where these two were journeying. As nearly as could be discerned, the second traveller was about fifty years old, apparently in the same rank of life as Goodman Brown, and bearing a considerable resemblance to him, though perhaps more

SECTION II: QUESTIONS

1
Are there any senses in which Goodman Brown's "excellent resolve" is excellent?

2
Why does Goodman Brown feel the need of justification, and why does he feel justified?

3
How do Goodman Brown's thoughts prepare us for the meeting and help to identify the stranger?

4
How do details of setting, thought and situation, and physical description identify the stranger, and what dimension is added by his resemblance to Goodman Brown?

5
What tensions of Section I are heightened by Goodman Brown's having "kept covenant"?

6
Write a paragraph defining the atmosphere of this section, explaining what it owes to Section I.

in expression than features. Still they might have been taken for father and son. And yet, though the elder person was as simply clad as the younger, and as simple in manner too, he had an indescribable air of one who knew the world, and who would not have felt abashed at the governor's dinner table or in King William's court, were it possible that his affairs should call him thither. But the only thing about him that could be fixed upon as remarkable was his staff, which bore the likeness of a great black snake, so curiously wrought that it might almost be seen to twist and wriggle itself like a living serpent. This, of course, must have been an ocular deception, assisted by the uncertain light.

"Come, Goodman Brown," cried his fellow-traveller, "this is a dull pace for the beginning of a journey. Take my staff, if you are so soon weary."

"Friend," said the other, exchanging his slow pace for a full stop, "having kept covenant by meeting thee here, it is my purpose now to return whence I came. I have scruples touching the matter thou wot'st of."

SECTION III

"Sayest thou so?" replied he of
the serpent, smiling apart. "Let us
walk on, nevertheless, reasoning as
we go; and if I convince thee not
thou shalt turn back. We are but a
little way in the forest yet."

"Too far! too far!" exclaimed the
goodman, unconsciously resum'ng
his walk. "My father never went
into the woods on such an errand,
nor his father before him. We have
been a race of honest men and good
Christians since the days of the martyrs; and shall I be the first of the
name of Brown that ever took his
path and kept"—

"Such company, thou wouldst
say," observed the elder person, interpreting his pause. "Well said,
Goodman Brown! I have been as
well acquainted with your family
as with ever a one among the Puritans; and that's no trifle to say. I
helped your grandfather, the constable, when he lashed the Quaker
woman so smartly through the
streets of Salem; and it was I that
brought your father a pitch-pine
knot, kindled at my own hearth, to
set fire to an Indian village, in King
Philip's war. They were my good
friends, both; and many a pleasant
walk have we had along this path,
and returned merrily after midnight.
I would fain be friends w:th you for
their sake."

"If it be as thou sayest," replied
Goodman Brown, "I marvel they
never spoke of these matters; or,
verily, I marvel not, seeing that the
least rumor of the sort would have
driven them from New England.
We are a people of prayer, and good
works to boot, and abide no such
wickedness."

"Wickedness or not," said the
traveller with the twisted staff, "I
have a very general acquaintance
here in New England. The deacons
of many a church have drunk the

SECTION III: QUESTIONS

1
What does the stranger mean by "reason
together," and how would you summarize
his argument? Is the stranger telling the
truth when he speaks of his wide acquaintance, and what effect do his tales have on
Goodman Brown?

2
What is Goodman's Brown's final defense,
and how do you explain the stranger's
reaction to it?

3
What is he saying about the relationship of
the leaders of Puritan society and evil in
his subsequent revelations of intimacy?

4
Write a paragraph defining the atmosphere
and tensions of this section and trace them
to their origins.

communion wine with me; the
selectmen of divers towns make me
their chairman; and a majority of
the Great and General Court are
firm supporters of my interest. The
governor and I, too—But these are
state secrets."

"Can this be so?" cried Goodman
Brown, with a stare of amazement
at his undisturbed companion.
"Howbeit, I have nothing to do with
the governor and council; they have
their own ways, and are no rule for
a simple husbandman like me. But,
were I to go on with thee, how
should I meet the eye of that good
old man, our minister, at Salem
village? Oh, his voice would make
me tremble both Sabbath day and
lecture day."

Thus far the elder traveller had
listened with due gravity; but now
burst into a fit of irrepressible mirth,
shaking himself so violently that
his snake-like staff actually seemed
to wriggle in sympathy.

"Ha! ha! ha!" shouted he again
and again; then composing himself,
"Well, go on, Goodman Brown, go
on; but, prithee, don't kill me with
laughing."

"Well, then, to end the matter at
once," said Goodman Brown, considerably nettled, "there is my wife,
Faith. It would break her dear little
heart; and I'd rather break my
own."

"Nay, if that be the case," answered the other, "e'en go thy ways,
Goodman Brown. I would not for
twenty old women like the one hobbling before us that Faith should
come to any harm."

SECTION IV

As he spoke he pointed his staff at a female figure on the path, in whom Goodman Brown recognized a very pious and exemplary dame, who had taught him his catechism in youth, and was still his moral and spiritual adviser, jointly with the minister and Deacon Gookin.

"A marvel, truly, that Goody Cloyse should be so far in the wilderness at nightfall," said he. "But with your leave, friend, I shall take a cut through the woods until we have left this Christian woman behind. Being a stranger to you, she might ask whom I was consorting with and whither I was going."

"Be it so," said his fellow-traveller. "Betake you to the woods, and let me keep the path."

Accordingly the young man turned aside, but took care to watch his companion, who advanced softly along the road until he had come within a staff's length of the old dame. She, meanwhile, was making the best of her way, with singular speed for so aged a woman, and mumbling some indistinct words— a prayer, doubtless—as she went. The traveller put forth his staff and touched her withered neck with what seemed the serpent's tail.

"The devil!" screamed the pious old lady.

"Then Goody Cloyse knows her old friend?" observed the traveller, confronting her and leaning on his writhing stick.

"Ah, forsooth, and is it your worship indeed?" cried the good dame. "Yea, truly is it, and in the very image of my old gossip, Goodman Brown, the grandfather of the silly fellow that now is. But—would your worship believe it?—my broomstick hath strangely disappeared, stolen, as I suspect, by that unhanged witch, Goody Cory, and that, too, when I was all anointed with the

SECTION IV: QUESTIONS

1
What is important about the description of Goody Cloyse as "a very pious and exemplary dame," "the moral and spiritual advisor" of Goodman Brown?

2
Why does Goodman Brown not want Goody Cloyse to see him?

3
What do their attitudes toward each other reveal about Goodman Brown and Goody Cloyse?

4
Who is the "nice young man," and what is the communion he is to be taken into?

5
What is the "world of meaning" in Goodman Brown's simple comment at the end of this section?

6
Write a paragraph showing how certain threads of previous sections are developed in this section.

juice of smallage, and cinquefoil,
and wolf's bane"—

"Mingled with fine wheat and the
fat of a new-born babe," said the
shape of old Goodman Brown.

"Ah, your worship knows the
recipe," cried the old lady, cackling
aloud. "So, as I was saying, being
all ready for the meeting, and no
horse to ride on, I made up my mind
to foot it; for they tell me there is a
nice young man to be taken into
communion tonight. But now your
good worship will lend me your
arm, and we shall be there in a
twinkling."

"That can hardly be," answered
her friend. "I may not spare you my
arm, Goody Cloyse; but here is my
staff, if you will."

So saying, he threw it down at her
feet, where, perhaps, it assumed life,
being one of the rods which its
owner had formerly lent to the
Egyptian magi. Of this fact, however, Goodman Brown could not
take cognizance. He had cast up his
eyes in astonishment, and, looking
down again, beheld neither Goody
Cloyse nor the serpentine staff, but
his fellow-traveller alone, who
waited for him as calmly as if nothing had happened.

"That old woman taught me my
catechism," said the young man;
and there was a world of meaning
in this simple comment.

SECTION V

They continued to walk onward, while the elder traveller exhorted his companion to make good speed and persevere in the path, discoursing so aptly that his arguments seemed rather to spring up in the bosom of his auditor than to be suggested by himself. As they went, he plucked a branch of maple to serve for a walking stick, and began to strip it of the twigs and little boughs, which were wet with evening dew. The moment his fingers touched them they became strangely withered and dried up as with a week's sunshine. Thus the pair proceeded, at a good free pace, until suddenly, in a gloomy hollow of the road, Goodman Brown sat himself down on the stump of a tree and refused to go any farther.

"Friend," said he, stubbornly, "my mind is made up. Not another step will I budge on this errand. What if a wretched old woman do choose to go to the devil when I thought she was going to heaven: is that any reason why I should quit my dear Faith and go after her?"

"You will think better of this by and by," said his acquaintance, composedly. "Sit here and rest yourself a while; and when you feel like moving again, there is my staff to help you along."

SECTION V: QUESTIONS

1

What is implied by the statement that the stranger's arguments seemed to spring up in the breast of his auditor?

2

What is suggested by the withering of the twigs at the stranger's touch?

3

Why does Goodman Brown decide to go no further, and how seriously does the stranger take this decision?

4

Write a paragraph defining the part this section plays in the conflict that has been evident in the preceding sections.

SECTION VI

Without more words, he threw his companion the maple stick, and was as speedily out of sight as if he had vanished into the deepening gloom. The young man sat a few moments by the roadside, applauding himself greatly, and thinking with how clear a conscience he should meet the minister in his morning walk, nor shrink from the eye of good old Deacon Gookin. And what calm sleep would be his that very night, which was to have been spent so wickedly, but so purely and sweetly now, in the arms of Faith! Amidst these pleasant and praise-worthy meditations, Goodman Brown heard the tramp of horses along the road, and deemed it advisable to conceal himself within the verge of the forest, conscious of the guilty purpose that had brought him thither, though now so happily turned from it.

On came the hoof tramps and the voices of the riders, two grave old voices, conversing soberly as they drew near. These mingled sounds appeared to pass along the road, within a few yards of the young man's hiding-place; but, owing doubtless to the depth of the gloom at that particular spot, neither the travellers nor their steeds were visible. Though their figures brushed the small boughs by the wayside, it could not be seen that they intercepted, even for a moment, the faint gleam from the strip of bright sky athwart which they must have passed. Goodman Brown alternately crouched and stood on tiptoe, pulling aside the branches and thrusting forth his head as far as he durst without discerning so much as a shadow. It vexed him the more, because he could have sworn, were such a thing possible, that he recognized the voices of the minister and Deacon Gookin, jogging along

SECTION VI: QUESTIONS

1

What hope stirred in the previous section is encouraged at the beginning of this?

2

How real or how unreal is the presence of the minister and Deacon Gookin?

3

What is revealed about Goodman Brown in his alternately crouching and standing on tiptoe?

4

On what kind of note does the section end?

5

Write a paragraph describing the extent to which the story so far can be read as a kind of education of Goodman Brown. What part do other people play in this education?

quietly, as they were wont to do,
when bound to some ordination or
ecclesiastical council. While yet
within hearing, one of the riders
stopped to pluck a switch.

"Of the two, reverend sir," said the
voice like the deacon's," "I had
rather miss an ordination dinner
than to-night's meeting. They tell
me that some of our community are
to be here from Falmouth and beyond, and others from Connecticut
and Rhode Island, besides several of
Indian powwows, who, after their
fashion, know almost as much
deviltry as the best of us. Moreover,
there is a goodly young woman to be
taken into communion."

"Mighty well, Deacon Gookin!"
replied the solemn old tones of the
minister. "Spur up, or we shall be
late. Nothing can be done, you
know, until I get on the ground."

The hoofs clattered again; and
the voices, talking so strangely in
the empty air, passed on through
the forest, where no church had ever
been gathered or solitary Christian
prayed. Whither, then, could these
holy men be journeying so deep into
the heathen wilderness? Young
Goodman Brown caught hold of a
tree for support, being ready to sink
down on the ground, faint and overburdened with the heavy sickness
of his heart. He looked up to the
sky, doubting whether there really
was a heaven above him. Yet there
was the blue arch, and the stars
brightening in it.

"With heaven above and Faith
below, I will yet stand firm against
the devil!" cried Goodman Brown.

SECTION VII

While he still gazed upward into
the deep arch of the firmament and
had lifted his hands to pray, a cloud,
though no wind was stirring, hurried across the zenith and hid the
brightening stars. The blue sky was
still visible, except directly overhead,
where this black mass of cloud was
sweeping swiftly northward. Aloft in
the air, as if from the depths of the
cloud, came a confused and doubtful
sound of voices. Once the listener
fancied that he could distinguish the
accents of towns-people of his own,
men, and women, both pious and
ungodly, many of whom he had met
at the communion table, and had
seen others rioting at the tavern.
The next moment, so indistinct were
the sounds, he doubted whether he
had heard aught but the murmur
of the old forest, whispering without
a wind. Then came a stronger swell
of those familiar tones, heard daily
in the sunshine at Salem village, but
never until now from a cloud of
night. There was one voice of a
young woman, uttering lamentations, yet with an uncertain sorrow,
and entreating for some favor,
which, perhaps, it would grieve her
to obtain; and all the unseen multitude, both saints and sinners,
seemed to encourage her onward.
"Faith!" shouted Goodman Brown,
in a voice of agony and desperation;
and the echoes of the forest mocked
him, crying, "Faith! Faith!" as if bewildered wretches were seeking her
all through the wilderness.
The cry of grief, rage, and terror
was yet piercing the night, when the
unhappy husband held his breath
for a response. There was a scream,
drowned immediately in a louder
murmur of voices, fading into far-
off laughter, as the dark cloud swept
away, leaving the clear and silent
sky above Goodman Brown. But
something fluttered lightly down

SECTION VII: QUESTIONS

1
In the context of Goodman Brown's final
assertion in the previous section, what does
the opening sentence of this section suggest?

2
How is the young woman's apparent conflict
similar to Goodman Brown's and what does
this explain about Faith?

3
On how many different levels can you interpret his cry, the answering scream, and
the pink ribbon?

4
To what conclusions about evil is Goodman
Brown driven by this last apparition or
vision or experience?

5
Write a paragraph explaining Goodman
Brown's situation at the end of this section
and explain the part which others have
played in bringing him to it.

through the air and caught on the
branch of a tree. The young man
seized it, and beheld a pink ribbon.

"My Faith is gone!" cried he, after
one stupefied moment. "There is no
good on earth; and sin is but a
name. Come, devil; for to thee is
this world given."

SECTION VIII:

And, maddened with despair, so
that he laughed loud and long, did
Goodman Brown grasp his staff and
set forth again, at such a rate that
he seemed to fly along the forest
path rather than to walk or run.
The road grew wilder and drearier
and more faintly traced, and vanished at length, leaving him in the
heart of the dark wilderness, still
rushing onward with the instinct
that guides mortal man to evil. The
whole forest was peopled with
frightful sounds—the creaking of
the trees, the howling of wild beasts,
and the yell of Indians; while sometimes the wind tolled like a distant
church bell, and sometimes gave a
broad roar around the traveller, as if
all Nature were laughing him to
scorn. But he was himself the chief
horror of the scene, and shrank not
from its other horrors.

"Ha! ha! ha!" roared Goodman
Brown when the wind laughed at
him. "Let us hear which will laugh
loudest. Think not to frighten me
with your deviltry. Come witch,
come wizard, come Indian powwow,
come devil himself, and here comes
Goodman Brown. You may as well
fear him as he fear you."

In truth, all through the haunted
forest there could be nothing more
frightful than the figure of Goodman Brown. On he flew among the
black pines, brandishing his staff
with frenzied gestures, now giving

84

SECTION VIII: QUESTIONS

1
Compare this part of his journey and his
zeal in making it with the beginning of the
journey in Sections I and II.

2
In what sense or senses is Goodman Brown
the "chief horror of the scene"?

3
Why does he laugh, and what is he laughing
at? Underline all the references to religion
in this section. What does their combination
with references to the "benighted wilderness" add to the setting?

4
In a paragraph, compare Goodman Brown's
situation in this section with his situation
in Section I.

vent to an inspiration of horrid
blasphemy, and now shouting forth
such laughter as set all the echoes of
the forest laughing like demons
around him. The fiend in his own
shape is less hideous than when he
rages in the breast of man. Thus
sped the demoniac on his course,
until, quivering among the trees, he
saw a red light before him, as when
the felled trunks and branches of a
clearing have been set on fire, and
throw up their lurid blaze against
the sky, at the hour of midnight. He
paused, in a lull of the tempest that
had driven him onward, and heard
the swell of what seemed a hymn,
rolling solemnly from a distance
with the weight of many voices. He
knew the tune; it was a familiar one
in the choir of the village meeting
house. The verse died heavily away,
and was lengthened by a chorus, not
of human voices, but of all the
sounds of the benighted wilderness
pealing in awful harmony together.
Goodman Brown cried out, and his
cry was lost to his own ear by its
unison with the cry of the desert.

In the interval of silence he stole
forward until the light glared full
upon his eyes. At one extremity of
an open space, hemmed in by the
dark wall of the forest, arose a rock,
bearing some rude, natural resemblance either to an altar or a pulpit,
and surrounded by four blazing
pines, their tops aflame, their stems
untouched, like candles at an evening meeting. The mass of foliage
that had overgrown the summit of
the rock was all on fire, blazing high
into the night and fitfully illuminating the whole field. Each pendent
twig and leafy festoon was in a
blaze. As the red light arose and fell,
a numerous congregation alternately
shone forth, then disappeared in
shadow, and again grew, as it were,
out of the darkness, peopling the
heart of the solitary woods at once.

SECTION IX

"A grave and dark-clad company," quoth Goodman Brown.

In truth they were such. Among them, quivering to and fro between gloom and splendor, appeared faces that would be seen next day at the council board of the province, and others which, Sabbath after Sabbath, looked devoutly heavenward, and benignantly over the crowded pews, from the holiest pulpits in the land. Some affirm that the lady of the governor was there. At least there were high dames well known to her, and wives of honored husbands, and widows, a great multitude, and ancient maidens, all of excellent repute, and fair young girls, who trembled lest their mothers should espy them. Either the sudden gleams of light flashing over the obscure field bedazzled Goodman Brown, or he recognized a score of the church members of Salem village famous for their especial sanctity. Good old Deacon Gookin had arrived, and waited at the skirts of that venerable saint, his revered pastor. But, irreverently consorting with these grave, reputable, and pious people, these elders of the church, these chaste dames and dewy virgins, there were men of dissolute lives and women of spotted fame, wretches given over to all mean and filthy vice, and suspected even of horrid crimes. It was strange to see that the good shrank not from the wicked, nor were the sinners abashed by the saints. Scattered also among their pale-faced enemies were the Indian priests, or pow-wows, who had often scared their native forest with more hideous incantations than any known to English witchcraft.

"But where is Faith?" thought Goodman Brown; and, as hope came into his heart, he trembled.

SECTION IX: QUESTIONS

1
In what senses other than the literal is the "grave and dark-clad company . . . quivering to and fro between gloom and splendor"?

2
To whom and why did it seem "strange" that "the good seemed not to shrink from the wicked"?

3
What does Goodman Brown hope for, and why does the hope make him tremble?

4
In a paragraph, identify the tensions of Section VIII and show how they are heightened in this section.

Another verse of the hymn arose,
a slow and mournful strain, such
as the pious love, but joined to
words which expressed all that our
nature can conceive of sin, and
darkly hinted at far more. Unfathomable to mere mortals is the
lore of fiends. Verse after verse was
sung; and still the chorus of the
desert swelled between like the
deepest tone of a mighty organ; and
with the final peal of that dreadful
anthem there came a sound, as if the
roaring wind, the rushing streams,
the howling beasts, and every other
voice of the unconcerted wilderness
were mingling and according with
the voice of guilty man in homage to
the prince of all. The four blazing
pines threw up a loftier flame, and
obscurely discovered shapes and
visages of horror on the smoke
wreaths above the impious assembly. At the same moment the fire
on the rock shot redly forth and
formed a glowing arch above its
base, where now appeared a figure.
With reverence, be it spoken, the
figure bore no slight similitude, both
in garb and manner, to some grave
divine of the New England churches.

87

88

SECTION X

"Bring forth the converts!" cried a voice that echoed through the field and rolled into the forest.

At the word, Goodman Brown stepped forth from the shadow of the trees and approached the congregation, with whom he felt a loathful brotherhood by the sympathy of all that was wicked in his heart. He could have well-nigh sworn that the shape of his own dead father beckoned him to advance, looking downward from a smoke wreath, while a woman, with dim features of despair, threw out her hand to warn him back. Was it his mother? But he had no power to retreat one step, nor to resist, even in thought, when the minister and good old Deacon Gookin seized his arms and led him to the blazing rock. Thither came also the slender form of a veiled female, led between Goody Cloyse, that pious teacher of the catechism, and Martha Carrier, who had received the devil's promise to be queen of hell. A rampant hag was she. And there stood the proselytes beneath the canopy of fire.

"Welcome, my children," said the dark figure, "to the communion of your race. Ye have found thus young your nature and your destiny. My children, look behind you!"

They turned; and flashing forth, as it were, in a sheet of flame, the fiend worshippers were seen; the smile of welcome gleamed darkly on every visage.

"There," resumed the sable form, "are all whom ye have reverenced from youth. Ye deemed them holier than yourselves, and shrank from your own sin, contrasting it with their lives of righteousness and prayerful aspirations heavenward. Yet here are they all in my worshipping assembly. This night it shall be granted you to know their secret deeds: how hoary-bearded elders

SECTION X: QUESTIONS

1

Why is it appropriate that the two "converts" should be escorted to the altar by these particular persons?

2

What are the usual meanings of "communion," and in what senses is what happens in this section "communion" and initiation for the converts?

3

What definition of the human race does the speech of the dark figure imply?

4

Write a paragraph defining the effect on Goodman Brown of the final revelation in this section.

of the church have whispered wanton words to the young maids of their households; how many a woman, eager for widows' weeds, has given her husband a drink at bedtime and let him sleep his last sleep in her bosom; how beardless youths have made haste to inherit their fathers' wealth; and how fair damsels—blush not, sweet ones— have dug little graves in the garden, and bidden me, the sole guest to an infant's funeral. By the sympathy of your human hearts for sin ye shall scent out all the places— whether in church, bedchamber, street, field, or forest—where crime has been committed, and shall exult to behold the whole earth one stain of guilt, one mighty blood spot. Far more than this. It shall be yours to penetrate, in every bosom, the deep mystery of sin, the fountain of all wicked arts, and which inexhaustibly supplies more evil impulses than human power—than my power at its utmost—can make manifest in deeds. And now, my children, look upon each other."

They did so; and, by the blaze of the hell-kindled torches, the wretched man beheld his Faith, and the wife her husband, trembling before that unhallowed altar.

89

90

SECTION XI

"Lo, there ye stand, my children,"
said the figure, in a deep and solemn
tone, almost sad with its despairing
awfulness, as if his once angelic
nature could yet mourn for our miserable race. "Depending upon one
another's hearts, ye had still hoped
that virtue were not all a dream.
Now are ye undeceived. Evil is the
nature of mankind. Evil must be
your only happiness. Welcome
again, my children, to the communion of your race."
  "Welcome," repeated the fiend
worshippers, in one cry of despair
and triumph.
  And there they stood, the only
pair, as it seemed, who were yet
hesitating on the verge of wickedness in this dark world. A basin was
hollowed, naturally, in the rock.
Did it contain water, reddened by
the lurid light? or was it blood? or,
perchance, a liquid flame? Herein
did the shape of evil dip his hand
and prepare to lay the mark of baptism upon their foreheads, that they
might be partakers of the mystery of
sin, more conscious of the secret
guilt of others, both in deed and
thought, than they could now be of
their own. The husband cast one
look at his pale wife, and Faith at
him. What polluted wretches would
the next glance show them to each
other, shuddering alike at what they
disclosed and what they saw!

SECTION XI: QUESTIONS

1
Remembering what Goodman Brown had
counted on his wife for at the end of Section I, state how he must now feel?

2
Consider all the ways in which it is appropriate that the "welcome" should be uttered
with both "despair and triumph."

3
What is appropriate about each description
of what the basin contains?

4
Is the special knowledge conferred by the
baptism important knowledge, and what is
its relationship to the idea of "triumph"?

5
Why will they "shudder at the spectacle of
themselves"?

6
In a paragraph describe the relationship of
the converts to the "shape of evil."

SECTION XII

"Faith! Faith!" cried the husband,
"look up to heaven, and resist the
wicked one."
  Whether Faith obeyed he knew

SECTION XII: QUESTIONS

1
Why is Goodman Brown now able to resist
the "wicked one," and what is the dramatic
effect of that resistance at this point in
the story?

not. Hardly had he spoken when he found himself amid calm night and solitude, listening to a roar of the wind which died heavily away through the forest. He staggered against the rock, and felt it chill and damp; while a hanging twig, that had been all on fire, besprinkled his cheek with the coldest dew.

SECTION XIII

The next morning young Goodman Brown came slowly into the street of Salem village, staring around him like a bewildered man. The good old minister was taking a walk along the graveyard to get an appetite for breakfast and meditate his sermon, and bestowed a blessing, as he passed, on Goodman Brown. He shrank from the venerable saint as if to avoid an anathema. Old Deacon Gookin was at domestic worship, and the holy words of his prayer were heard through the open window. "What God doth the wizard pray to?" quoth Goodman Brown. Goody Cloyse, that excellent old Christian, stood in the early sunshine at her own lattice, catechizing a little girl who had brought her a pint of morning's milk. Goodman Brown snatched away the child as from the grasp of the fiend himself. Turning the corner by the meeting-house, he spied the head of Faith, with the pink ribbons, gazing anxiously forth, and bursting into such joy at sight of him that she skipped along the street and almost kissed her husband before the whole village. But Goodman Brown looked sternly and sadly into her face, and passed on without a greeting.

2

In a paragraph describe the consequences of his resistance and how the details dramatize them.

SECTION XIII: QUESTIONS

1

What details illustrate a change in Goodman Brown's nature, and is there any effect gained by their being presented in this particular order?

2

In a paragraph discuss how his present state of mind contrasts with his state of mind in the first section of the story.

SECTION XIV

Had Goodman Brown fallen asleep in the forest and only dreamed a wild dream of a witch-meeting?

Be it so if you will; but, alas! it was a dream of evil omen for young Goodman Brown. A stern, a sad, a darkly meditative, a distrustful, if not a desperate man did he become from the night of that fearful dream. On the Sabbath day, when the congregation were singing a holy psalm, he could not listen because an anthem of sin rushed loudly upon his ear and drowned all the blessed strain. When the minister spoke from the pulpit with power and fervid eloquence, and, with his hand on the open Bible, of the sacred truths of our religion, and of saint-like lives and triumphant deaths, and of future bliss or misery unutterable, then did Goodman Brown turn pale, dreading lest the roof should thunder down upon the gray blasphemer and his hearers. Often, waking suddenly at midnight, he shrank from the bosom of Faith; and at morning or eventide, when the family knelt down at prayer, he scowled and muttered to himself, and gazed sternly at his wife, and turned away. And when he had lived long, and was borne to his grave a hoary corpse, followed by Faith, an aged woman, and children and grandchildren, a goodly procession, besides neighbors not a few, they carved no hopeful verse upon his tombstone, for his dying hour was gloom.

SECTION XIV: QUESTIONS

1
Does the text of the story suggest an answer to the question stated here?

2
Does it matter whether or not Goodman Brown's experience was a dream?

3
In a paragraph describe the kind of life Goodman Brown now lives as a result of his experience.

Young Goodman Brown
Topics for Essays

NOTE. Whichever of these topics you write on and whatever the position you take, remember that your view must rest on an understanding of the details of the story. Your generalizations have to be supported by specific references to the text and by interpretation of those references. Any opinion which is unsupported by evidence is worthless, while any opinion supported by evidence must command respect.

1
Define the vision of life expressed through the story and describe how the sequence, or the character, or the setting, or the situation, or any combination of these elements helps to communicate it.

2
Trace the successive shifts in Goodman Brown's attitude toward his journey and toward his wife and discuss their relationship to the final vision of the story.

3
Discuss the significance of the movement from Salem to the forest and from the forest back to Salem.

4
Defend or attack the following statement: "The story conveys the feeling that, though it is saddening, the knowledge of man's evil is necessary and of ultimate value to the sensitive person."

94 In Part Two we divided the stories into sections and asked specific questions about the details. If you have been following directions, you will by now have begun to develop an eye for significant details, and your reading will have slowed down enough for you to start asking yourself the kind of questions that a reader must ask if he wants to become involved in the story he is reading.

The following six stories have been divided into sections, but this time *you* will be expected to ask the questions about the relationships and implications of specific details. We suggest that you proceed as follows.

First, read through the story very quickly, ignoring the divisions. Try to get a sense of what the story is about in general. You might wish to make a few brief notes to yourself, trying to sum up your first impressions, but don't be too specific on the basis of a first reading.

Next, go back to the first section, and pick out those details that seem to you most significant, the ones that give you the sharpest sense of a character, a setting, a situation, or whatever it is that this section seems to be developing. Ask yourself the same kind of questions you were asked in Part Two. What does this particular word or phrase reveal about a character or add to a scene? How do the physical details help define the nature of the character? What is the setting or atmosphere of this particular house, or city, or place, and what does it contribute? What are the motives of the characters, and what forces make them act the way they do? Why do they say the particular things they say? What situations are the characters confronted by, and how do they respond to them?

In any good work of fiction, the answers to these questions will be found in the details; but in order to find these answers, you must first ask the questions. Having asked the questions, be certain that you also try to answer them. Repeat this process for each section of the story.

We suggest that you write out your questions and your answers and bring them to class to try on your classmates and instructor. If they are good questions, they will provide an excellent basis for class discussion. But whether you write them out formally, or keep them in your head, it is imperative that you continue the practice of writing brief paragraphs on each section, defining the functions of the various details, pointing out how and what each section contributes to the vision the story is trying to help you to experience.

When you have finished "reading" the story, you should have written as many paragraphs as there are sections. With these paragraphs as your starting points, you are ready to discuss the story in class. If a paper is assigned, you have a firm basis for writing an intelligent, well-supported essay.

After each story you will find several suggested topics for essays. The topics have been carefully chosen to guide you in the construction of some aspects of the vision the story reveals. Even if you have not been assigned a paper, they will help you get a sense of the story. Each topic should give you some hint of what to look for in your examination of the details in each section.

JOHN GALSWORTHY   THE JAPANESE QUINCE

I

As Mr. Nilson, well known in the City, opened the window of his dressing room on Campden Hill, he experienced a peculiar sweetish sensation in the back of his throat, and a feeling of emptiness just under his fifth rib. Hooking the window back, he noticed that a little tree in the Square Gardens had come out in blossom, and that the thermometer stood at sixty. "Perfect morning," he thought; "spring at last!"

Resuming some meditations on the price of Tintos, he took up an ivory-backed handglass and scrutinised his face. His firm, well-coloured cheeks, with their neat brown moustaches, and his round, well-opened, clear grey eyes, wore a reassuring appearance of good health. Putting on his black frock coat, he went downstairs.

In the dining room his morning paper was laid out on the sideboard. Mr. Nilson had scarcely taken it in his hand when he again became aware of that queer feeling. Somewhat concerned, he went to the French window and descended the scrolled iron steps into the fresh air. A cuckoo clock struck eight.

"Half an hour to breakfast," he thought; "I'll take a turn in the Gardens."

II

He had them to himself, and proceeded to pace the circular path with his morning paper clasped behind him. He had scarcely made two revolutions, however, when it was borne in on him that, instead of going away in the fresh air, the feeling had increased. He drew several deep breaths, having heard deep breathing recommended by his wife's doctor; but they augmented rather than diminished the sensation—as if some sweetish liquor in course within him, together with a faint aching just above his heart. Running over what he had eaten the night before, he could recollect no unusual dish, and it occurred to him that

---

it might possibly be some smell affecting him. But he could detect nothing except a faint sweet lemony scent, rather agreeable than otherwise, which evidently
emanated from the bushes budding in the sunshine. He was on the point of
resuming his promenade, when a blackbird close by burst into song, and, looking
up, Mr. Nilson saw at a distance of perhaps five yards a little tree, in the heart
of whose branches the bird was perched. He stood staring curiously at this tree,
recognising it for that which he had noticed from his window. It was covered
with young blossoms, pink and white, and little bright green leaves both round
and spiky; and on all this blossom and these leaves the sunlight glistened. Mr.
Nilson smiled; the little tree was so alive and pretty! And instead of passing on,
he stayed there smiling at the tree.

III

"Morning like this!" he thought; "and here I am the only person in the Square
who has the—to come out and—!" But he had no sooner conceived this thought
than he saw quite near him a man with his hands behind him, who was also
staring up and smiling at the little tree. Rather taken aback, Mr. Nilson ceased to
smile, and looked furtively at the stranger. It was his next-door neighbour, Mr.
Tandram, well known in the City, who had occupied the adjoining house for
some five years. Mr. Nilson perceived at once the awkwardness of his position,
for, being married, they had not yet had occasion to speak to one another. Doubtful as to his proper conduct, he decided at last to murmur: "Fine morning!" and
was passing on, when Mr. Tandram answered: "Beautiful, for the time of year!"
Detecting a slight nervousness in his neighbour's voice, Mr. Nilson was em-
boldened to regard him openly. He was of about Mr. Nilson's own height, with
firm, well-coloured cheeks, neat brown moustaches, and round, well-opened,
clear grey eyes; and he was wearing a black frock coat. Mr. Nilson noticed that
he had his morning paper clasped behind him as he looked up at the little tree.
And, visited somehow by the feeling that he had been caught out, he said
abruptly:

"Er—can you give me the name of that tree?"

Mr. Tandram answered:

"I was about to ask you that," and stepped towards it. Mr. Nilson also approached the tree.

"Sure to have its name on, I should think," he said.

Mr. Tandram was the first to see the little label, close to where the blackbird
had been sitting. He read it out.

"Japanese quince!"

"Ah!" said Mr. Nilson, "thought so. Early flowerers."

"Very," assented Mr. Tandram, and added: "Quite a feelin' in the air today."

Mr. Nilson nodded.

"It was a blackbird singin'," he said.

"Blackbirds," answered Mr. Tandram. "I prefer them to thrushes myself; more
body in the note." And he looked at Mr. Nilson in an almost friendly way.

"Quite," murmured Mr. Nilson. "These exotics, they don't bear fruit. Pretty blossom!" and he again glanced up at the blossom, thinking: "Nice fellow, this, I rather like him."

IV

Mr. Tandram also gazed at the blossom. And the little tree, as if appreciating their attention, quivered and glowed. From a distance the blackbird gave a loud, clear call. Mr. Nilson dropped his eyes. It struck him suddenly that Mr. Tandram looked a little foolish; and, as if he had seen himself, he said: "I must be going in. Good morning!"

A shade passed over Mr. Tandram's face, as if he, too, had suddenly noticed something about Mr. Nilson.

"Good morning," he replied, and clasping their journals to their backs they separated.

Mr. Nilson retraced his steps towards his garden window, walking slowly so as to avoid arriving at the same time as his neighbour. Having seen Mr. Tandram mount his scrolled iron steps, he ascended his own in turn. On the top step he paused.

V

With the slanting spring sunlight darting and quivering into it, the Japanese quince seemed more living than a tree. The blackbird had returned to it, and was chanting out his heart.

Mr. Nilson sighed; again he felt that queer sensation, that choky feeling in his throat.

The sound of a cough or sigh attracted his attention. There, in the shadow of his French window, stood Mr. Tandram, also looking forth across the Gardens at the little quince tree.

Unaccountably upset, Mr. Nilson turned abruptly into the house, and opened his morning paper.

The Japanese Quince
Topics for Essays

NOTE. Whichever of these topics you write on and whatever the position you take, remember that your view must rest on an understanding of the details of the story. Your generalizations have to be supported by specific references to the text and by interpretation of those references. Any opinion which is unsupported by evidence is worthless, while any opinion supported by evidence must command respect.

1
Define the vision of life expressed through the story and describe how the sequence, or the character, or the setting, or the situation, or any combination of these elements helps to communicate it.

2
What illness, physical and psychological, does Mr. Nilson seem to be suffering from, and what part does it play in the story?

3
Define the importance to the story of the quince tree, the blackbird, and the newspapers.

4
Show how the details of the story dramatize a conflict between the forces of nature and the forces of social convention.

5
Defend or attack the following statement: "Civilization necessarily separates men from nature and from each other and automatically weakens them."

I

The great Pullman was whirling onward with such dignity of motion that a glance from the window seemed simply to prove that the plains of Texas were pouring eastward. Vast flats of green grass, dull-hued spaces of mesquit and cactus, little groups of frame houses, woods of light and tender trees, all were sweeping into the east, sweeping over the horizon, a precipice.

II

A newly married pair had boarded this coach at San Antonio. The man's face was reddened from many days in the wind and sun, and a direct result of his new black clothes was that his brick-colored hands were constantly performing in a most conscious fashion. From time to time he looked down respectfully at his attire. He sat with a hand on each knee, like a man waiting in a barber's shop. The glances he devoted to other passengers were furtive and shy.

The bride was not pretty, nor was she very young. She wore a dress of blue cashmere, with small reservations of velvet here and there, and with steel buttons abounding. She continually twisted her head to regard her puff sleeves, very stiff, straight, and high. They embarrassed her. It was quite apparent that she had cooked, and that she expected to cook, dutifully. The blushes caused by the careless scrutiny of some passengers as she had entered the car were strange to see upon this plain, under-class countenance, which was drawn in placid, almost emotionless lines.

They were evidently very happy. "Ever been in a parlor car before?" he asked, smiling with delight.

"No," she answered, "I never was. It's fine, ain't it?"

"Great! And then after a while we'll go forward to the diner, and get a big lay-out. Finest meal in the world. Charge a dollar."

"Oh, do they?" cried the bride. "Charge a dollar? Why, that's too much—for us—ain't it, Jack?"

"Not this trip, anyhow," he answered bravely. "We're going to go the whole thing."

Later he explained to her about the trains. "You see, it's a thousand miles from one end of Texas to the other; and this train runs right across it, and never stops but four times." He had the pride of an owner. He pointed out to her the dazzling fittings of the coach; and in truth her eyes opened wider as she contemplated the sea-green figured velvet, the shining brass, silver, and glass, the wood that gleamed as darkly brilliant as the surface of a pool of oil. At one end a bronze figure sturdily held a support for a separated chamber, and at convenient places on the ceiling were frescos in olive and silver.

To the minds of the pair, their surroundings reflected the glory of their marriage that morning in San Antonio; this was the environment of their new estate; and the man's face in particular beamed with an elation that made him appear ridiculous to the Negro porter. This individual at times surveyed them from afar with an amused and superior grin. On other occasions he bullied them with skill in ways that did not make it exactly plain to them that they were being bullied. He subtly used all the manners of the most unconquerable kind of snobbery. He oppressed them; but of this oppression they had small knowledge, and they speedily forgot that infrequently a number of travelers covered them with stares of derisive enjoyment. Historically there was supposed to be something infinitely humorous in their situation.

III

"We are due in Yellow Sky at 3:42," he said, looking tenderly into her eyes.

"Oh, are we?" she said, as if she had not been aware of it. To evince surprise at her husband's statement was part of her wifely amiability. She took from a pocket a little silver watch; and as she held it before her, and stared at it with a frown of attention, the new husband's face shone.

"I bought it in San Anton' from a friend of mine," he told her gleefully.

"It's seventeen minutes past twelve," she said, looking up at him with a kind of shy and clumsy coquetry. A passenger, noting this play, grew excessively sardonic, and winked at himself in one of the numerous mirrors.

At last they went to the dining car. Two rows of Negro waiters, in glowing white suits, surveyed their entrance with the interest, and also the equanimity, of men who had been forewarned. The pair fell to the lot of a waiter who happened to feel pleasure in steering them through their meal. He viewed them with the manner of a fatherly pilot, his countenance radiant with benevolence. The patronage, entwined with the ordinary deference, was not plain to them. And yet, as they returned to their coach, they showed in their faces a sense of escape.

IV

To the left, miles down a long purple slope, was a little ribbon of mist where moved the keening Rio Grande. The train was approaching it at an angle, and the apex was Yellow Sky. Presently it was apparent that, as the distance from Yellow Sky grew shorter, the husband became commensurately restless. His brick-red hands were more insistent in their prominence. Occasionally he was even rather absent-minded and faraway when the bride leaned forward and addressed him.

As a matter of truth, Jack Potter was beginning to find the shadow of a deed weigh upon him like a leaden slab. He, the town marshal of Yellow Sky, a man known, liked, and feared in his corner, a prominent person, had gone to San

Antonio to meet a girl he believed he loved, and there, after the usual prayers, had actually induced her to marry him, without consulting Yellow Sky for any part of the transaction. He was now bringing his bride before an innocent and unsuspecting community.

Of course people in Yellow Sky married as it pleased them, in accordance with a general custom; but such was Potter's thought of his duty to his friends, or of their idea of his duty, or of an unspoken form which does not control men in these matters, that he felt he was heinous. He had committed an extraordinary crime. Face to face with this girl in San Antonio, and spurred by his sharp impulse, he had gone headlong over all the social hedges. At San Antonio he was like a man hidden in the dark. A knife to sever any friendly duty, any form, was easy to his hand in that remote city. But the hour of Yellow Sky — the hour of daylight — was approaching.

He knew full well that his marriage was an important thing to his town. It could only be exceeded by the burning of the new hotel. His friends could not forgive him. Frequently he had reflected on the advisability of telling them by telegraph, but a new cowardice had been upon him. He feared to do it. And now the train was hurrying him toward a scene of amazement, glee, and reproach. He glanced out of the window at the line of haze swinging slowly in toward the train.

Yellow Sky had a kind of brass band, which played painfully, to the delight of the populace. He laughed without heart as he thought of it. If the citizens could dream of his prospective arrival with his bride, they would parade the band at the station and escort them, amid cheers and laughing congratulations, to his adobe home.

He resolved that he would use all the devices of speed and plainscraft in making the journey from the station to his house. Once within that safe citadel, he could issue some sort of vocal bulletin, and then not go among the citizens until they had time to wear off a little of their enthusiasm.

The bride looked anxiously at him. "What's worrying you, Jack?"

He laughed again. "I'm not worrying, girl; I'm only thinking of Yellow Sky."

She flushed in comprehension.

A sense of mutual guilt invaded their minds and developed a finer tenderness. They looked at each other with eyes softly aglow. But Potter often laughed the same nervous laugh; the flush upon the bride's face seemed quite permanent.

The traitor to the feelings of Yellow Sky narrowly watched the speeding landscape. "We're nearly there," he said.

Presently the porter came and announced the proximity of Potter's home. He held a brush in his hand, and, with all his airy superiority gone, he brushed Potter's new clothes as the latter slowly turned this way and that way. Potter fumbled out a coin and gave it to the porter, as he had seen others do. It was a heavy and muscle-bound business, as that of a man shoeing his first horse.

The porter took their bag, and as the train began to slow they moved forward to the hooded platform of the car. Presently the two engines and their long string of coaches rushed into the station of Yellow Sky.

"They have to take water here," said Potter, from a constricted throat and in mournful cadence, as one announcing death. Before the train stopped his eye had swept the length of the platform, and he was glad and astonished to see there was none upon it but the station agent, who, with a slightly hurried and anxious air, was walking toward the water tanks. When the train had halted, the porter alighted first, and placed in position a little temporary step.

"Come on, girl," said Potter, hoarsely. As he helped her down they each laughed on a false note. He took the bag from the Negro, and bade his wife cling to his arm. As they slunk rapidly away, his hangdog glance perceived that they were unloading the two trunks, and also that the station agent, far ahead near the baggage car, had turned and was running toward him, making gestures. He laughed, and groaned as he laughed, when he noted the first effect of his marital bliss upon Yellow Sky. He gripped his wife's arm firmly to his side, and they fled. Behind them the porter stood, chuckling fatuously.

103

VI

The California express on the Southern Railway was due at Yellow Sky in twenty-one minutes. There were six men at the bar of the Weary Gentleman saloon. One was a drummer who talked a great deal and rapidly; three were Texans who did not care to talk at that time; and two were Mexican sheep-herders, who did not talk as a general practice in the Weary Gentleman saloon. The barkeeper's dog lay on the boardwalk that crossed in front of the door. His head was on his paws, and he glanced drowsily here and there with the constant vigilance of a dog that is kicked on occasion. Across the sandy street were some vivid green grass-plots, so wonderful in appearance, amid the sands that burned near them in a blazing sun, that they caused a doubt in the mind. They exactly resembled the grass mats used to represent lawns on the stage. At the cooler end of the railway station, a man without a coat sat in a tilted chair and smoked his pipe. The fresh-cut bank of the Rio Grande circled near the town, and there could be seen beyond it a great plum-colored plain of mesquit.

VII

Save for the busy drummer and his companions in the saloon, Yellow Sky was dozing. The newcomer leaned gracefully upon the bar, and recited many tales with the confidence of a bard who has come upon a new field.

"—and at the moment that the old man fell downstairs with the bureau in his arms, the old woman was coming up with two scuttles of coal, and of course—"

The drummer's tale was interrupted by a young man who suddenly appeared in the open door. He cried: "Scratchy Wilson's drunk, and has turned loose with both hands." The two Mexicans at once set down their glasses and faded out of the rear entrance of the saloon.

The drummer, innocent and jocular, answered: "All right, old man. S'pose he has? Come in and have a drink, anyhow."

But the information had made such an obvious cleft in every skull in the room that the drummer was obliged to see its importance. All had become instantly solemn. "Say," said he, mystified, "what is this?" His three companions made the introductory gesture of eloquent speech; but the young man at the door forestalled them.

"It means, my friend," he answered, as he came into the saloon, "that for the next two hours this town won't be a health resort."

The barkeeper went to the door, and locked and barred it; reaching out of the window, he pulled in heavy wooden shutters, and barred them. Immediately a solemn, chapel-like gloom was upon the place. The drummer was looking from one to another.

"But say," he cried, "what is this, anyhow? You don't mean there is going to be a gun fight?"

"Don't know whether there'll be a fight or not," answered one man, grimly, "but there'll be some shootin'—some good shootin'."

The young man who had warned them waved his hand. "Oh, there'll be a fight fast enough, if any one wants it. Anybody can get a fight out there in the street. There's a fight just waiting."

The drummer seemed to be swayed between the interest of a foreigner and a perception of personal danger.

"What did you say his name was?" he asked.

"Scratchy Wilson," they answered in chorus.

"And will he kill anybody? What are you going to do? Does this happen often? Does he rampage around like this once a week or so? Can he break in that door?"

"No, he can't break down that door," replied the barkeeper. "He's tried it three times. But when he comes you'd better lay down on the floor, stranger. He's dead sure to shoot at it, and a bullet may come through."

Thereafter the drummer kept a strict eye upon the door. The time had not yet been called for him to hug the floor, but, as a minor precaution, he sidled near to the wall. "Will he kill anybody?" he said again.

The men laughed low and scornfully at the question.

"He's out to shoot, and he's out for trouble. Don't see any good in experimentin' with him."

"But what do you do in a case like this? What do you do?"

A man responded: "Why, he and Jack Potter—"

"But," in chorus the other men interrupted, "Jack Potter's in San Anton'."

"Well, who is he? What's he got to do with it?"

"Oh, he's the town marshal. He goes out and fights Scratchy when he gets on one of these tears."

"Wow!" said the drummer, mopping his brow. "Nice job he's got."

VIII

The voices had toned away to mere whisperings. The drummer wished to ask further questions, which were born of an increasing anxiety and bewilderment; but when he attempted them, the men merely looked at him in irritation and motioned him to remain silent. A tense waiting hush was upon them. In the deep shadows of the room their eyes shone as they listened for sounds from the street. One man made three gestures at the barkeeper; and the latter, moving like a ghost, handed him a glass and a bottle. The man poured a full glass of whisky, and set down the bottle noiselessly. He gulped the whisky in a swallow, and turned again toward the door in immovable silence. The drummer saw that the barkeeper, without a sound, had taken a Winchester from beneath the bar. Later he saw this individual beckoning to him, so he tiptoed across the room.

"You better come with me back of the bar."

"No, thanks," said the drummer, perspiring; "I'd rather be where I can make a break for the back door."

Whereupon the man of bottles made a kindly but peremptory gesture. The drummer obeyed it, and, finding himself seated on a box with his head below the level of the bar, balm was laid upon his soul at sight of various zinc and copper fittings that bore a resemblance to armor plate. The barkeeper took a seat comfortably upon an adjacent box.

"You see," he whispered, "this here Scratchy Wilson is a wonder with a gun— a perfect wonder; and when he goes on the war-trail, we hunt our holes— naturally. He's about the last one of the old gang that used to hang out along the river here. He's a terror when he's drunk. When he's sober he's all right— kind of simple—wouldn't hurt a fly—nicest fellow in town. But when he's drunk—whoo!"

There were periods of stillness. "I wish Jack Potter was back from San Anton'," said the barkeeper. "He shot Wilson up once—in the leg—and he would sail in and pull out the kinks in this thing."

Presently they heard from a distance the sound of a shot, followed by three wild howls. It instantly removed a bond from the men in the darkened saloon. There was a shuffling of feet. They looked at each other. "Here he comes," they said.

IX

A man in a maroon-colored flannel shirt, which had been purchased for purposes of decoration, and made principally by some Jewish women on the East Side of New York, rounded a corner and walked into the middle of the main street of Yellow Sky. In either hand the man held a long, heavy, blue-black revolver. Often he yelled, and these cries rang through a semblance of a deserted village, shrilly flying over the roofs in a volume that seemed to have no relation to the ordinary vocal strength of a man. It was as if the surrounding stillness formed the arch of a tomb over him. These cries of ferocious challenge rang against walls of silence. And his boots had red tops with gilded imprints, of the kind beloved in winter by little sledding boys on the hillsides of New England.

The man's face flamed in a rage begot of whisky. His eyes, rolling, and yet keen for ambush, hunted the still doorways and windows. He walked with the creeping movement of the midnight cat. As it occurred to him, he roared menacing information. The long revolvers in his hands were as easy as straws; they were moved with an electric swiftness. The little fingers of each hand played sometimes in a musician's way. Plain from the low collar of the shirt, the cords of his neck straightened and sank, straightened and sank, as passion moved him. The only sounds were his terrible invitations. The calm adobes preserved their demeanor at the passing of this small thing in the middle of the street.

X

There was no offer of fight—no offer of fight. The man called to the sky. There were no attractions. He bellowed and fumed and swayed his revolvers here and everywhere.

The dog of the barkeeper of the Weary Gentleman saloon had not appreciated the advance of events. He yet lay dozing in front of his master's door. At sight of the dog, the man paused and raised his revolver humorously. At sight of the man, the dog sprang up and walked diagonally away, with a sullen head, and growling. The man yelled, and the dog broke into a gallop. As it was about to enter an alley, there was a loud noise, a whistling, and something spat the ground directly before it. The dog screamed, and, wheeling in terror, galloped headlong in a new direction. Again there was a noise, a whistling, and sand was kicked viciously before it. Fear-stricken, the dog turned and flurried like an animal in a pen. The man stood laughing, his weapons at his hips.

Ultimately the man was attracted by the closed door of the Weary Gentleman saloon. He went to it and, hammering with a revolver, demanded drink.

The door remaining imperturbable, he picked a bit of paper from the walk, and nailed it to the framework with a knife. He then turned his back contemptuously upon this popular resort and, walking to the opposite side of the street and spinning there on his heel quickly and lithely, fired at the bit of paper. He missed it by a half-inch. He swore at himself, and went away. Later he comfortably fusilladed the windows of his most intimate friend. The man was playing with this town; it was a toy for him.

But still there was no offer of fight. The name of Jack Potter, his ancient antagonist, entered his mind, and he concluded that it would be a glad thing if he should go to Potter's house, and by bombardment induce him to come out and fight. He moved in the direction of his desire, chanting Apache scalp-music.

When he arrived at it, Potter's house presented the same still front as had the other adobes. Taking up a strategic position, the man howled a challenge. But this house regarded him as might a great stone god. It gave no sign. After a decent wait, the man howled further challenges, mingling with them wonderful epithets.

Presently there came the spectacle of a man churning himself into deepest rage over the immobility of a house. He fumed at it as the winter wind attacks a prairie cabin in the North. To the distance there should have gone the sound of a tumult like the fighting of two hundred Mexicans. As necessity bade him, he paused for breath or to reload his revolvers.

XI

Potter and his bride walked sheepishly and with speed. Sometimes they laughed together shamefacedly and low.

"Next corner, dear," he said finally.

They put forth the efforts of a pair walking bowed against a strong wind. Potter was about to raise a finger to point the first appearance of the new home when, as they circled the corner, they came face to face with a man in a maroon-colored shirt, who was feverishly pushing cartridges into a large revolver. Upon the instant the man dropped his revolver to the ground and, like lightning, whipped another from its holster. The second weapon was aimed at the bridegroom's chest.

There was a silence. Potter's mouth seemed to be merely a grave for his tongue. He exhibited an instinct to at once loosen his arm from the woman's grip, and he dropped the bag to the sand. As for the bride, her face had gone as yellow as old cloth. She was a slave to hideous rites, gazing at the apparitional snake.

The two men faced each other at a distance of three paces. He of the revolver smiled with a new and quiet ferocity.

"Tried to sneak up on me," he said. "Tried to sneak up on me!" His eyes grew more baleful. As Potter made a slight movement, the man thrust his revolver venomously forward. "No, don't you do it, Jack Potter. Don't you move a finger toward a gun just yet. Don't you move an eyelash. The time has come for me to settle with you, and I'm goin' to do it my own way, and loaf along with no interferin'. So if you don't want a gun bent on you, just mind what I tell you."

Potter looked at his enemy. "I ain't got a gun on me, Scratchy," he said. "Honest, I ain't." He was stiffening and steadying, but yet somewhere at the back of his mind a vision of the Pullman floated: the sea-green figured velvet, the shining brass, silver, and glass, the wood that gleamed as darkly brilliant as the surface of a pool of oil—all the glory of the marriage, the environment of the new estate. "You know I fight when it comes to fighting, Scratchy Wilson; but I ain't got a gun on me. You'll have to do all the shootin' yourself."

His enemy's face went livid. He stepped forward, and lashed his weapon to and fro before Potter's chest. "Don't you tell me you ain't got no gun on you, you whelp. Don't tell me no lie like that. There ain't a man in Texas ever seen you without no gun. Don't take me for no kid." His eyes blazed with light, and his throat worked like a pump.

"I ain't takin' you for no kid," answered Potter. His heels had not moved an inch backward. "I'm takin' you for a damn fool. I tell you I ain't got a gun, and I ain't. If you're goin' to shoot me up, you better begin now; you'll never get a chance like this again."

XII

So much enforced reasoning had told on Wilson's rage; he was calmer. "If you ain't got a gun, why ain't you got a gun?" he sneered. "Been to Sunday school?"

"I ain't got a gun because I've just come from San Anton' with my wife. I'm married," said Potter. "And if I'd thought there was going to be any galoots like you prowling around when I brought my wife home, I'd had a gun, and don't you forget it."

"Married!" said Scratchy, not at all comprehending.

"Yes, married. I'm married," said Potter, distinctly.

"Married?" said Scratchy. Seemingly for the first time, he saw the drooping, drowning woman at the other man's side. "No!" he said. He was like a creature allowed a glimpse of another world. He moved a pace backward, and his arm, with the revolver, dropped to his side. "Is this the lady?" he asked.

"Yes, this is the lady," answered Potter.

There was another period of silence.

"Well," said Wilson at last, slowly, "I s'pose it's all off now."

"It's all off if you say so, Scratchy. You know I didn't make the trouble." Potter lifted his valise.

"Well, I 'low it's off, Jack," said Wilson. He was looking at the ground. "Married!" He was not a student of chivalry; it was merely that in the presence of this foreign condition he was a simple child of the earlier plains. He picked up his starboard revolver, and, placing both weapons in their holsters, he went away. His feet made funnel-shaped tracks in the heavy sand.

The Bride Comes to Yellow Sky
Topics for Essays

NOTE. Whichever of these topics you write on and whatever the position you take, remember that your view must rest on an understanding of the details of the story. Your generalizations have to be supported by specific references to the text and by interpretation of those references. Any opinion which is unsupported by evidence is worthless, while any opinion supported by evidence must command respect.

1
Define the vision of life expressed through the story and describe how the sequence, or the character, or the setting, or the situation, or any combination of these elements helps to communicate it.

2
Of what importance to the story are the different worlds suggested by the two settings?

3
What does Jack Potter's act of taking a bride suggest about a change in his previous relationship with the town? What specific details help to define this new relationship?

4
How does the sequence of sections build to the confrontation scene between Potter and Scratchy Wilson, and help to make Wilson's response meaningful?

5
What opposing forces in the town are represented by the bride and by Scratchy Wilson and what role does Jack Potter play in relation to these two forces?

6
Defend or attack the following statement: "The marriage of Jack Potter signifies the coming of the slow death of civilization to Yellow Sky."

I

He was a small man with a beard and was very nervous. I remember how the cords of his neck were drawn taut.

For years he had been trying to cure people of illness by the method called psychoanalysis. The idea was the passion of his life. "I came here because I am tired," he said dejectedly. "My body is not tired but something inside me is old and worn-out. I want joy. For a few days or weeks I would like to forget men and women and the influences that make them the sick things they are."

There is a note that comes into the human voice by which you may know real weariness. It comes when one has been trying with all his heart and soul to think his way along some difficult road of thought. Of a sudden he finds himself unable to go on. Something within him stops. A tiny explosion takes place. He bursts into words and talks, perhaps foolishly. Little side currents of his nature he didn't know were there run out and get themselves expressed. It is at such times that a man boasts, uses big words, makes a fool of himself in general.

And so it was the doctor became shrill. He jumped up from the steps where he had been sitting, talking, and walked about. "You come from the West. You have kept away from people. You have preserved yourself—damn you! I haven't—" His voice had indeed become shrill. "I have entered into lives. I have gone beneath the surface of the lives of men and women. Women especially I have studied—our own women, here in America."

"You have loved them?" I suggested.

"Yes," he said. "Yes—you are right there. I have done that. It is the only way I can get at things. I have to try to love. You see how that is? It's the only way. Love must be the beginning of things with me."

I began to sense the depths of his weariness. "We will go swim in the lake," I urged.

"I don't want to swim or do any damn plodding thing. I want to run and shout," he declared. "For a while, for a few hours, I want to be like a dead leaf blown by the winds over these hills. I have one desire and one only—to free myself."

II

We walked in a dusty country road. I wanted him to know that I thought I understood, so I put the case in my own way.

When he stopped and stared at me I talked. "You are no more and no better that myself," I declared. "You are a dog that has rolled in offal, and because you are not quite a dog you do not like the smell of your own hide."

In turn my voice became shrill. "You blind fool," I cried impatiently. "Men like you are fools. You cannot go along that road. It is given to no man to venture far along the road of lives." I became passionately in earnest. "The illness you pretend to cure is the universal illness," I said. "The thing you want to do cannot be done. Fool—do you expect love to be understood?"

We stood in the road and looked at each other. The suggestion of a sneer played about the corners of his mouth. He put a hand on my shoulder and shook me. "How smart we are—how aptly we put things!"

He spat the words out and then turned and walked a little away. "You think you understand, but you don't understand," he cried. "What you say can't be done can be done. You're a liar. You cannot be so definite without missing something vague and fine. You miss the whole point. The lives of people are like young trees in a forest. They are being choked by climbing vines. The vines are old thoughts and beliefs planted by dead men. I am myself covered by crawling creeping vines that choke me."

He laughed bitterly. "And that's why I want to run and play," he said. "I want to be a leaf blown by the wind over hills. I want to die and be born again, and I am only a tree covered with vines and slowly dying. I am, you see, weary and want to be made clean. I am an amateur, venturing timidly into lives," he concluded. "I am weary and want to be made clean. I am covered by creeping crawling things."

III

A woman from Iowa came here to Chicago and took a room in a house on the west-side. She was about twenty-seven years old and ostensibly she came to the city to study advanced methods for teaching music.

A certain young man also lived in the west-side house. His room faced a long hall on the second floor of the house and the one taken by the woman was across the hall facing his room.

In regard to the young man—there is something very sweet in his nature. He is a painter but I have often wished he would decide to become a writer. He tells things with understanding and he does not paint brilliantly.

And so the woman from Iowa lived in the west-side house and came home from the city in the evening. She looked like a thousand other women one sees in the streets every day. The only thing that at all made her stand out among

111

the women in the crowds was that she was a little lame. Her right foot was slightly deformed and she walked with a limp. For three months she lived in the house—where she was the only woman except the landlady—and then a feeling in regard to her began to grow up among the men of the house.

The men all said the same thing concerning her. When they met in the hallway at the front of the house, they stopped, laughed and whispered. "She wants a lover," they said and winked. "She may not know it but a lover is what she needs." One knowing Chicago and Chicago men would think that an easy want to be satisfied. I laughed when my friend—whose name is LeRoy—told me the story, but he did not laugh. He shook his head. "It wasn't so easy," he said. "There would be no story were the matter that simple."

112

LeRoy tried to explain. "Whenever a man approached her she became alarmed," he said. Men kept smiling and speaking to her. They invited her to dinner and to the theatre, but nothing would induce her to walk in the streets with a man. She never went into the streets at night. When a man stopped and tried to talk with her in the hallway she turned her eyes to the floor and then ran into her room. Once a young drygoods clerk who lived there induced her to sit with him on the steps before the house.

He was a sentimental fellow and took hold of her hand. When she began to cry he was alarmed and arose. He put a hand on her shoulder and tried to explain, but under the touch of his fingers her whole body shook with terror. "Don't touch me," she cried, "don't let your hands touch me!" She began to scream and people passing in the street stopped to listen. The drygoods clerk was alarmed and ran upstairs to his own room. He bolted the door and stood listening. "It is a trick," he declared in a trembling voice. "She is trying to make trouble. I did nothing to her. It was an accident and anyway what's the matter? I only touched her arm with my fingers."

IV

Perhaps a dozen times LeRoy has spoken to me of the experience of the Iowa woman in the west-side house. The men there began to hate her. Although she would have nothing to do with them she would not let them alone. In a hundred ways she continually invited approaches that when made she repelled. When she stood naked in the bathroom facing the hallway where the men passed up and down she left the door slightly ajar. There was a couch in the living room downstairs, and when men were present she would sometimes enter and without saying a word throw herself down before them. On the couch she lay with lips drawn slightly apart. Her eyes stared at the ceiling. Her whole physical being seemed to be waiting for something. The sense of her filled the room. The men standing about pretended not to see. They talked loudly. Embarrassment took possession of them and one by one they crept quietly away.

V

One evening the woman was ordered to leave the house. Someone, perhaps the drygoods clerk, had talked to the landlady and she acted at once. "If you leave tonight I shall like it that much better," LeRoy heard the elder woman's voice saying. She stood in the hallway before the Iowa woman's room. The landlady's voice rang through the house.

LeRoy the painter is tall and lean and his life has been spent in devotion to ideas. The passions of his brain have consumed the passions of his body. His income is small and he has not married. Perhaps he has never had a sweetheart. He is not without physical desire but he is not primarily concerned with desire.

On the evening when the Iowa woman was ordered to leave the west-side house, she waited until she thought the landlady had gone downstairs, and then went into LeRoy's room. It was about eight o'clock and he sat by a window reading a book. The woman did not knock but opened the door. She said nothing but ran across the floor and knelt at his feet. LeRoy said that her twisted foot made her run like a wounded bird, that her eyes were burning and that her breath came in little gasps. "Take me," she said, putting her face down upon his knees and trembling violently. "Take me quickly. There must be a beginning to things. I can't stand the waiting. You must take me at once."

You may be quite sure LeRoy was perplexed by all this. From what he has said I gathered that until that evening he had hardly noticed the woman. I suppose that of all the men in the house he had been the most indifferent to her. In the room something happened. The landlady followed the woman when she ran to LeRoy, and the two women confronted him. The woman from Iowa knelt trembling and frightened at his feet. The landlady was indignant. LeRoy acted on impulse. An inspiration came to him. Putting his hand on the kneeling woman's shoulder he shook her violently. "Now behave yourself," he said quickly. "I will keep my promise." He turned to the landlady and smiled. "We have been engaged to be married," he said. "We have quarreled. She came here to be near me. She has been unwell and excited. I will take her away. Please don't let yourself be annoyed. I will take her away."

When the woman and LeRoy got out of the house she stopped weeping and put her hand into his. Her fears had all gone away. He found a room for her in another house and then went with her into the park and sat on a bench.

VI

Everything LeRoy has told me concerning this woman strengthens my belief in what I said to the man that day in the mountains. You cannot venture along the road of lives. On the bench he and the woman talked until midnight and he saw and talked with her many times later. Nothing came of it. She went back, I suppose, to her place in the West.

In the place from which she had come the woman had been a teacher of music. She was one of four sisters, all engaged in the same sort of work, and, LeRoy says, all quiet capable women. Their father had died when the eldest girl was not yet ten, and five years later the mother died also. The girls had a house and a garden.

In the nature of things I cannot know what the lives of the women were like but of this one may be quite certain—they talked only of women's affairs,

113

thought only of women's affairs. No one of them ever had a lover. For years no man came near the house.

Of them all only the youngest, the one who came to Chicago, was visibly affected by the utterly feminine quality of their lives. It did something to her. All day and every day she taught music to young girls and then went home to the women. When she was twenty-five she began to think and to dream of men. During the day and through the evening she talked with women of women's affairs, and all the time she wanted desperately to be loved by a man. She went to Chicago with that hope in mind. LeRoy explained her attitude in the matter and her strange behavior in the west-side house by saying she had thought too much and acted too little. "The life force within her became decentralized," he declared. "What she wanted she could not achieve. The living force within could not find expression. When it could not get expressed in one way it took another. Sex spread itself out over her body. It permeated the very fibre of her being. At the last she was sex personified, sex become condensed and impersonal. Certain words, the touch of a man's hand, sometimes even the sight of a man passing in the street did something to her."

VII

Yesterday I saw LeRoy and he talked to me again of the woman and her strange and terrible fate. We walked in the park by the lake. As we went along the figure of the woman kept coming into my mind. An idea came to me.

"You might have been her lover," I said. "That was possible. She was not afraid of you."

LeRoy stopped. Like the doctor who was so sure of his ability to walk into lives he grew angry and scolded. For a moment he stared at me and then a rather odd thing happened. Words said by the other man in the dusty road in the hills came to LeRoy's lips and were said over again. The suggestion of a sneer played about the corners of his mouth. "How smart we are. How aptly we put things," he said.

The voice of the young man who walked with me in the park by the lake in the city became shrill. I sensed the weariness in him. Then he laughed and said quietly and softly, "It isn't so simple. By being sure of yourself you are in danger of losing all the romance of life. You miss the whole point. Nothing in life can be settled so definitely. The woman—you see—was like a young tree choked by a climbing vine. The thing that wrapped her about had shut out the light. She was a grotesque as many trees in the forest are grotesques. Her problem was such a difficult one that thinking of it has changed the whole current of my life. At first I was like you. I was quite sure. I thought I would be her lover and settle the matter."

LeRoy turned and walked a little away. Then he came back and took hold of my arm. A passionate earnestness took possession of him. His voice trembled. "She needed a lover, yes, the men in the house were quite right about that," he said. "She needed a lover and at the same time a lover was not what she needed. The need of a lover was, after all, a quite secondary thing. She needed to be loved; to be long and quietly and patiently loved. To be sure she is a grotesque, but then all the people in the world are grotesques. We all need to be loved. What would cure her would cure the rest of us also. The disease she had is, you see, universal. We all want to be loved and the world has no plan for creating our lovers."

VIII

LeRoy's voice dropped and he walked beside me in silence. We turned away from the lake and walked under trees. I looked closely at him. The cords of his neck were drawn taut. "I have seen under the shell of life and I am afraid," he mused. "I am myself like the woman. I am covered with creeping crawling vine-like things. I cannot be a lover. I am not subtle or patient enough. I am paying old debts. Old thoughts and beliefs—seeds planted by dead men—spring up in my soul and choke me."

For a long time we walked and LeRoy talked, voicing the thoughts that came into his mind. I listened in silence. His mind struck upon the refrain voiced by the man in the mountains. "I would like to be a dead dry thing," he muttered looking at the leaves scattered over the grass. "I would like to be a leaf blown away by the wind." He looked up and his eyes turned to where among the trees we could see the lake in the distance. "I am weary and want to be made clean. I am a man covered by creeping crawling things. I would like to be dead and blown by the wind over limitless waters," he said. "I want more than anything else in the world to be clean."

Seeds
Topics for Essays

NOTE. Whichever of these topics you write on and whatever the position you take, remember that your view must rest on an understanding of the details of the story. Your generalizations have to be supported by specific references to the text and by interpretation of those references. Any opinion which is unsupported by evidence is worthless, while any opinion supported by evidence must command respect.

1

Define the vision of life expressed through the story and describe how the sequence, or the character, or the setting, or the situation, or any combination of these elements helps to communicate it.

2

In what ways does the story of the girl from Iowa specifically illustrate the ideas of the psychiatrist and LeRoy?

3

Examine how the use of the "seed" metaphor, as suggested by the words of the psychiatrist and LeRoy, helps to reveal the vision of the story.

4

Defend or attack the following statement: "The sane and wholesome attitudes of the narrator balance the introspective perversions of the psychiatrist and LeRoy."

ROBERT PENN WARREN   THE LIFE AND WORK
                           OF PROFESSOR ROY MILLEN

I

Professor Roy Millen had loved his wife devotedly, and now, in the spring of the year 1937, she was dead. He had not realized before how much she had meant to him, how his own life had described its orbit, as it were, within the steady and beneficent influence of her being. If she had dominated the course of his life, it had not been by isolated, individual acts of superior will, but rather by defining, subtly but more completely year after year, the very atmosphere he breathed. His position at the university, the long tranquil evenings at the bridge table with the light glinting subduedly on the exciting and rich designs of the royal cards, the friends at the table, the respectful greeting in the corridors and on the street, the very food he put into his mouth—all of these items had been defined by her. He had never protested against this, not even fleetingly, in the privacy of his own mind. Day after day, year after year, he had accepted it as part of the inevitable furniture of his life, just as he had accepted the sound of her voice and the expression of her face. If he felt anything, it was a kind of gratitude. Any little act he could do for her—and it comforted him now to remember that he had always tried to do the little things she wanted, especially after her health failed—had only been the proper manifestation of his gratitude, or at least of his candid admission that she had made him what he was.

II

The self which he now was—the man with the carefully brushed tufts of white hair on each side of the pink and hygienic-looking bald skull, the rimless pince-nez with the black cord, the well-pressed but somewhat worn suits, blue or medium gray according to the season, the cleanly cut nails, the thoughts that came into his head—that self, too, had been defined by her. And during the twenty-odd years of his life with her, he had remembered more and more rarely the other self which he had been before his marriage. He did not like to remember that other time, for those years had been painful and long, so painful that even in recollection something of the distress of the old reality could revive within him. He had bent over the long rows of cotton, with the sun bearing down on his shoulders and the humid air swimming around him. He had clerked in crossroads stores. He had taught in the country schools of his native section, listening all day to the sullen or droning voices of the children and then tramping down some muddy road to his rented room in a tumble-down farmhouse. Later, long after those years were past, he would occasionally wonder, when the unsought recollections came to him, what had sustained him, what hope had given him strength enough to go on. Looking back, he could not say. He could not remember what strength had been in him, or remember what he had hoped for, or expected. Certainly, he had not hoped for what he had actually found. Anyway, he told himself humbly, this was better than what he had hoped for. For he had scarcely known that there could be such a life as this.

By the time he was twenty-nine he had managed to get a degree from a small denominational college. For two years then, he had better teaching jobs, and saved enough to see him through a winter at the state university. When he was thirty-seven, he received a Ph.D. in English literature. That June day he stood on the platform of the auditorium, stooped and sweating under the black robe and colored hood, as though to their weight were added the weight of all the privations and distresses which had brought him to that moment, and his outstretched hand shook. That fall, quite unexpectedly, he got a small job teaching freshmen at the university. One of the regular instructors was ill, and the head of the department thriftily surmised that Millen would take the job for little or nothing. During the year the instructor died.

III

"Millen is a good steady man," Dr. Saunders, the head of the department, remarked to his daughter one day toward the end of the year. "It looks as if we might just keep him on another year until we can make a permanent appointment."

"Yes," Mildred Saunders said dutifully, abstractedly. She was a tallish woman, a little past thirty, with a spindly figure and plain features. Her habitual expression was kindly, however, and she had a quiet nature. A few weeks after her father's remark, she saw Millen at a faculty reception, miserable and lonely in a corner, and talked to him, remembering what her father had said. In ministering to his embarrassment and shyness, she forgot something of her own habitual diffidence. The following year, early in the session, when Dr. Saunders had Millen to his house on some piece of academic business, Mildred Saunders saw him and asked him to come again. He came more and more frequently during the year, to sit in the shadowed and dingy parlor, his bony hands with the bitten nails moving uneasily on his knees. In May he received a permanent appointment to his job, and Mildred Saunders announced her engagement to him. She had married him, and he had been devoted to her, and now she was dead.

IV

She had died quite suddenly and ironically, just at the time when, after years of ill health, she seemed to be getting well and strong again, and they were planning to go away on a year's leave. They were planning to go to England, where he could work in one of the great English libraries and finish his book. Six years before, he had had a leave, and they had planned to go to England to work on the book, but they had gone, in the end, to southern California. He had not protested, even to himself, at the change in plans; in fact he suggested the change. The cold, damp climate of Millersburg in winter had always been bad for his wife's asthma and neuralgia, and England might be worse. And his wife's cousins in Los Angeles would be company for her while he worked on his book. And there were some very nice libraries in California. Everybody knew that.

She had seemed better at first in California, but then, despite everything, her health had taken a turn for the worse. She had been in the hospital, and the doctors had done all they could, and the cousins had been helpful and considerate. Some days they had even gone to the hospital and he had been able to stay at home and work or go to the library. But she had been very ill, and he knew what to do for her—better, he told himself, than the cousins or even the nurses. Even after she was able to leave the hospital and go back to Millersburg she was never really well. But she was very patient and rarely lost her temper with him. Sometimes, when he sat beside her bed—for during that period she was confined to her bed almost half of the time—she would reach out to touch his hand and say: "Just leave me alone, Roy, and go work on your book. You ought to work on your book, Roy. I don't mind being alone. I've gotten used to being alone." He would say that it didn't matter, or that it was moving along nicely, that he had done quite a bit lately. Or she would say: "I'm sorry we have to spend so much money on me, Roy, when you want to go away to work on your book." Then he would try to comfort her.

V

She was dead now, but there was the book left for him. I have my book to do, at least I have that, he concluded as soon as the first shock of grief had worn off and he had begun to search in himself for some center of meaning for his life. Then, day after day, as he came to accept the fact of his loss and his mind dwelt more and more on his book, a kind of modest excitement grew within him—an excitement so pleasurable that once or twice, remembering in the midst of it his wife's death, he was filled with a sense of shame and remorse.

He made his plans to go abroad, to England, to work in the libraries there, as he and his wife had planned. It was what she would have him do, he told himself. And the book would be a kind of monument to her. He would dedicate the book to her. As he walked slowly back from the campus to his house in the late afternoons or early evenings of spring, he would try to compose the dedication, saying the words aloud to himself as he looked up at the paling, peach-colored sky beyond the newly leafed branches. He had decided to sail in June, as soon as he could leave after commencement.

VI

"I hear you're going away for a year, Professor Millen," Tom Howell said, standing respectfully before Professor Millen's office desk. Then he added, in a dutiful tone, "To work on your book."

"Yes," Professor Millen said, "to work on my book." Then, as though recollecting himself, he made a little gesture toward the chair in front of the desk, and said, "Won't you have a seat, Howell?"

"Are you going to finish it in a year?" Howell asked, and sat down.

"I still have a little research to do. I have to settle a few points—points which can't be settled in libraries in this country. I have to do some work yet in one of the great English libraries." Professor Millen paused, looking over the green lawn outside his office window. "But I'll get it written within the year. Practically everything is in order. Though, of course," he paused again, looking at Tom Howell, who listened respectfully and with what seemed to be interest, "I'll have to do a good deal of retouching—style and so on, you know—" he waved his hand modestly in the air, "when I get back."

"I'm hoping—" the boy hesitated, fumbling in his pocket to draw out a folded paper, "I'm hoping to be able to go abroad next year. If I can make it. That's what I wanted to see you about, Professor Millen."

"Anything I can do, I'll be glad to do."

"It's a scholarship. A French scholarship, and I was hoping you'd recommend me. I've had a lot of work with you, and all. The French Department will recommend me, but I've done my minor in English, you know. What you'd say would count a lot."

"Howell," Professor Millen said, judicially putting the tips of his fingers together and inspecting the boy, "I've never had a better student than you are. Possibly never one as good. I'll say that in my recommendation. I'll write a strong one." He felt his enthusiasm mounting as he spoke, and a warmth suffused him as though at the prospect of some piece of happiness, some success, for himself.

VII

"I certainly appreciate it," the boy said. "This is about the only thing I've got in sight for next year, and I'm graduating. Oh, I reckon I could get a little teaching job or something for a year or two to save up some money to go on. I don't think I ought to ask my family for any more—they've been swell, putting me through college and giving me that trip to France two years back—"

"Yes, yes," Professor Millen said abstractedly, "oh, yes, you did go over one summer, didn't you?"

"Oh, that was just for fun," Howell said, "but this time it would be for work. And when I get back I ought to be able to get a pretty good job so I could save enough to get my Ph.D. quick. Up East."

"A year of study in France will be a fine opportunity," Professor Millen said. That enthusiasm and warmth which had filled him like a promise of happiness was waning now, he did not know why. He wished the boy would get up and go and leave him alone.

"Oh, it'll be an opportunity," Howell agreed, "and I'm not going to waste it. The work'll be fun, and there ought to be a little fun besides. I was in Paris for two weeks—and you know how Paris is, it sort of knocks you off your feet. You've been there?"

"Yes, yes," Professor Millen said hurriedly, impersonally, almost impatiently, averting his face from the boy and looking off across the patch of lawn, wondering why he had lied, why he had told the boy he had been to Paris. He watched some students, two boys and a girl, who moved across the sunlit, open space. They moved lingeringly. It seemed that they would never be across that bright, open space of green where the sun was. Then they were gone, hidden by the screen of foliage.

Professor Millen turned and brought his gaze to rest again on the the boy. The boy was leaning forward, his face smiling. Professor Millen saw, as for the first time, the blond, crisp hair combed back from the square forehead, the confident gaze of the blue eyes, the comfortable, confident way the coat hung from the good shoulders.

The boy stood up. "I've stayed too long. I know you've got a lot of work to do."

"No," Professor Millen said.

"And I certainly appreciate your recommendation. The address of the scholarship committee is on here," he said, and laid a printed sheet on the desk. "That's the circular, and all the information."

"I'll attend to it right away," Professor Millen said.

"Thank you," the boy said, and was gone.

VIII

For a few minutes Professor Millen sat there, his eyes on the bare wall opposite his desk. Then he read the circular. He laid it back on the desk and pressed a button. When the secretary came in, he handed her the printed sheet. "The address is on that," he said, and waited while she copied it. Then he said, "I'll give you the letter." He studied the bare wall for a moment, then began: "Gentlemen. I can truthfully say that I take the most sincere pleasure in recommending to you Mr. Thomas Howell. In my long career as a teacher I have never had a better student. He has an acute and penetrating intelligence, and, as is so often not the case with young men of his capacity, the patience and honesty of a true scholar. I am sure that if he is appointed to—" He hesitated, looking at the wall. "I am sure that—" he said at last, then stopped.

The secretary, her pencil poised above her pad, waited while Professor Millen seemed to withdraw, to sink within himself. Her foot made a slight reproachful scraping sound as she changed her position in the chair. She, too, began to look out the window, where Professor Millen's gaze now was fixed.

"That's all—for the present," Professor Millen said, suddenly. "Just hold that and I'll finish later. I've just thought—" he managed to look directly at her— "of something else I've got to do. There's something else."

After the secretary had left the office, closing the door softly behind her, he did not move for some time. Then he again looked out the window. The shadows were lengthening over the smooth lawn. The faintest premonitory flush was

121

touching the puffs of white cloud visible toward the top of his window. Before long now he would be going home. He picked up the circular. He read it again, very carefully, dwelling on it almost painfully, as though he were an illiterate trying to extort some secret from the words. He lifted his eyes from the sheet and stared at the chair where the boy had sat leaning forward, the pleasure shining on his clear, handsome face, the good coat riding easy on his shoulders, saying "—you know how Paris is, it sort of knocks you off your feet. You've been there?"

IX

Professor Millen let the circular slip from his lap to the floor. Then, decisively, he reached into the drawer of his desk and took out a sheet of paper. He wrote rapidly in his large, firm script:

Gentlemen:

I have been asked to recommend Mr. Thomas Howell to you for a scholarship for study in France. As you will observe from a transcript of his academic record, with which no doubt you have been provided, he has made the grade of A in all of his work in the English department of this institution, and I understand that his grades in French (his major subject) have been very high. This achievement, of course, deserves consideration, but candor compels me to say that a superficial facility and cleverness seem to characterize his mind. I do not wish to prejudice the committee against his case, and I may be wrong in my estimate; certainly, I hope that the committee will consider him very carefully. But I do feel that he lacks solidity of character, the spirit of patient inquiry, and what might be termed the philosophical bent.

Very respectfully yours,
Roy Millen,
Professor of English

Without looking up, he addressed an envelope hurriedly, the pen making a dry, scratching sound. Then he blotted and stamped the envelope, inserted the sheet, put the letter into his pocket, picked up his hat, and left the office. He would, he remembered, pass a postbox on his way home.

The Life and Work of Professor Roy Millen
Topics for Essays

NOTE. Whichever of these topics you write on and whatever the position you take, remember that your view must rest on an understanding of the details of the story. Your generalizations have to be supported by specific references to the text and by interpretation of those references. Any opinion which is unsupported by evidence is worthless, while any opinion supported by evidence must command respect.

1
Define the vision of life expressed through the story and describe how the sequence, or the character, or the setting, or the situation, or any combination of these elements helps to communicate it.

2
What does Professor Millen's relationship with his wife have to do with his writing a poor recommendation for his student?

3
How do Professor Millen's "life and work" define his competence as teacher and scholar?

4
Defend or attack the following statement: "Professor Millen's letter of recommendation contains an accurate estimate of Howell's character and abilities."

124

I

Mrs. Taylor shuffled a worn pack of cards and began her evening session at solitaire. She would play probably forty games before she went to bed, and she would win thirty of them. What harm if she cheated a little? Russian Bank was more fun, but it cannot be played alone, and her husband was bored by it. He had been unable to learn bridge in spite of the patient and more or less expert teaching of the Hammonds, who lived three blocks away.

The thirty-four-dollar synthetic radio had done nothing but croak since the day following its installation. The cheap piano's D and G above middle C were mute. The town's Carnegie Library acquired very few "hot" books and the few were nearly always out. Picture plays hurt Louis' eyes and he would not let her go out nights by herself, though he had no scruples against leaving her at home from eight to eleven Wednesdays, when he attended lodge and bowled.

So Mrs. Taylor shuffled her cards and tried to listen when Louis read aloud from the Milton Daily Star or the Milton Weekly Democrat, or recounted stories she had heard six times before and would hear six times again.

She had awakened this morning to the realization that it was the twelfth day of November, the ninth anniversary of her marriage. Louis had remembered that date for the first six years of their life together; for the last three years it had been to him just November the twelfth.

II

Nine years ago the Star and the Democrat had called her one of Milton's most charming and beautiful young women, and they had been right. They had referred to Louis as a model young man, sober, industrious and "solid"; a young man whom any girl should be proud and glad to have as a husband. They were right again.

Now Mrs. Taylor, at thirty-three, was good-looking, but in a cold, indifferent sort of way. She no longer bothered to embellish her natural attractiveness and she lacked the warmth and vivacity which had won the adoration of most of

Milton's male youth, notably Walter Frayne, Jim Satterly and Louis Taylor himself.

Louis was still a model young man, sober, industrious and "solid." When you thought of the precarious existence of the women who had married his chief rivals, you couldn't help feeling that wisdom and good luck had been on Mrs. Taylor's side when she made her choice.

Walter had attended college for one semester, at the end of which he came home with a perfect record of studies, 4; Flunks, 4. He had run amuck in Milton and ultimately, turned down by the girl he really cared for, had married an orphan whose parents had left her $150,000—but not for long. After this tidy sum had been poured away Walter was almost continuously unemployed and people wondered how he and his wife lived. And why.

There was nothing of the gay dog about Jim Satterly. He had graduated from high school and gone into the Milton Gas Company's office as bookkeeper at eight dollars per week. He was now thirty-five years old and still with the gas company, but his salary had been steadily increased until it was twenty-two dollars. His wife gave weekly piano lessons to a class of four pupils at fifty cents a half-hour each. She had borne Jim three children, or kiddies. The Slatterlys seemed to enjoy their kiddies and an occasional picture show, but no magazine editor had ever sent a staff man to get a success story out of Jim.

Louis Taylor was secretary to the town's only wealthy man, old Thomas Parvis, who owned a controlling interest in the Interurban Railway. Louis worked long hours and was paid four thousand a year, big money in Milton. It was enough to keep the childless Taylors in comfort; in comparative luxury, even. Couples with smaller incomes owned cars, took trips to near-by lake resorts and to Harper City, where a stock company presented worth-while plays. But Louis was saving for a rainy day and his wife had long ago given up praying for rain.

III

Mrs. Taylor was winning her fourth successive victory over solitaire by the simple expedient of pretending that a black queen was red.

"It says here," stated her husband, "that there are 27,650,267 automobiles in the world, according to a census just completed."

It was Mrs. Taylor's own fault that Louis had contracted the habit of reciting interesting tidbits from the paper. Back in May, 1924, he had asked her whether she would like to hear the news of the Loeb-Leopold case. She had already read it, but said yes, thinking it would be more thrilling even in repetition, than one of Louis' own experiences, also in repetition. Since then, she had listened every evening—except Wednesday, when Louis went out, and Sundays, when there was no paper—to excerpts from the Star, consisting principally of what is known in newspaper offices as filler—incontrovertible statistics about men and things in all parts of the world, facts that seemed to smite her husband like a bolt from the blue.

"Think of it!" he said. "Nearly twenty-eight million automobiles!"

"Heavens!" said Mrs. Taylor.

125

"And speaking of automobiles: 'Storms have made roads so bad in parts of Chile that drivers have not dared to go into the rural districts.' That's the trouble with owning a car. If you don't stay right on the paved streets or paved roads, you're liable to get stuck and maybe walk home. Besides that, you've got to be a mechanic yourself or else, when there's something wrong, you have to take it to a garage and lay it up a week till they consent to look at it and find out what's the matter, and then they don't know themselves nine times out of ten. But they charge you just the same and they charge you plenty. Did I tell you about Walter Trumbull's trip to Harper City?"

"Yes," said Mrs. Taylor.

"I don't believe I did. It was only last Friday night; no Thursday night, the night after the Spartans beat us by one pin, when I had a chance to get a 202 and hit the head pin just a little too full and they split on me. That was the night Berger showed up so drunk he couldn't bowl and we had to use Tommy and he shot 123.

"So it was the night after that when Walter and Marjorie started over to the City to see the 'Seventh Heaven,' and about five miles the other side of Two Oaks the engine died and Walter couldn't get it going again. His flash-light wouldn't work and Marjorie wouldn't let him strike matches with the hood up to see what the trouble was. As it turned out, it wouldn't have done him any good anyway.

"Finally he left poor Marjorie in the car and walked way back to Two Oaks, but the garage was closed up for the night and the whole town was asleep, so he went back to the car and by that time of course it was too late to see the show. He hailed three or four cars coming from the other way, trying to get a ride home, but it wasn't till after ten o'clock that he could get a car to stop and pick them up. The next morning he sent Charlie Thomas out to fix up the car so it would run or else tow it in, and Charlie found out there was nothing the matter with it except it was out of gas. When Walter told me about it, I said that was what he deserved for not patronizing the Interurban."

"We don't patronize it ourselves."

"I hear enough about it in the daytime without riding on it at night."

IV

Mrs. Taylor shuffled the cards and Louis resumed perusal of the Star.

"The old U. S. is a pretty good country after all," he said presently. "Listen to this: 'The Netherlands' unemployed now include 26,000 skilled and 24,000 unskilled workers.' And listen: 'A large proportion of Belgium's population still wear wooden shoes.' You wouldn't think that was possible in this day and age!"

"I imagine," said Mrs. Taylor, "that there are some places in the United States where people don't wear any shoes at all."

"Oh, sure, but not a large proportion; probably a few of those backwoods Tennessee mountaineers. And of course the colored people in the small towns in Georgia and South Carolina. You see lots of them, passing through on the train, that never had a shoe on in their life. I remember a place named Jesup, Georgia, a kind of junction. There was——No, that wasn't Jesup; it was some other place, some place the boss and I went through on the way to Daytona that time. I guess I told you about it."

"Yes," said Mrs. Taylor.

"You wouldn't believe the way some of those people live. Not all colored people, either; white people, too. Poor white trash, they call them. Or rather, 'po' white trash.' Families of four and five in one room. Mr. Parvis said it was a crime and kept wishing he could do something for them."

"Why didn't he?"

"Well, he's hardly got money enough to house and clothe the whole South and it wouldn't do any good to just pick out some one town and try and better conditions there."

"Why not?"

"It would be a drop in the bucket, and besides, other towns would hear about it and pester the life out of him. I reminded him he was taking the trip to get away from care and worry for a while and he ought not to fret himself about other people's business. Then, too, if he was going to practise some of his philanthropy down there, I'd probably be put in charge of it. We might even have to live there a year or two. I guess you wouldn't like that, would you?"

"It wouldn't make any difference to me," said Mrs. Taylor.

"What! Live in one of those God-forsaken holes, without any friends or anybody you'd want to make friends with! Nothing to do all day and all night but eat and sleep and—"

"Play solitaire," suggested Mrs. Taylor.

"You may think you wouldn't mind it, but that's because you've never seen it. Those Georgia villages are an interesting study, but as for making your home in one of them, you'd die of loneliness. Of course there's some spots in Florida that are pretty close to heaven. Take Daytona, for instance. But I've told you what it's like."

"Yes."

"They've got a beach that's so hard and smooth that they have automobile races on it. It's beautiful. And it's right close to Ormond, where Rockefeller spends his winters. Mr. Parvis and I saw him playing golf on the Ormond course. I can't see anything in golf myself, but maybe I would if I had a chance to get interested in it. When I'm as old as he is, I'll try it out, providing I've got as much time and one-millionth as much money."

"There's no reason why you shouldn't have fully as much money."

"I know what you mean by that. You're digging at my thriftiness, though I suppose you call it stinginess. You'll look at it differently when we're old."

"I hope I won't be here to look at it at all."

V

"No, you don't. But what was I saying? Oh, yes. Daytona is where I'd like to live in winter, if I had the means. I must have told you about running into Harry Riker down there."

"You did."

"It certainly was a funny thing, running into him! We hadn't seen each other for twenty-two years and he recognized me the minute he set eyes on me. I wouldn't have known him from Adam's off ox.

"It sure did take me back, running into Harry. He recalled one time, just before I left Shelbyville, when his father and mother were away on a visit somewhere. Harry's aunt, Mr. Riker's sister, was supposed to be taking care of Harry while his father and mother was away, but she was kind of old and she used to go to sleep right after supper.

"Well, there were a couple of girls, sisters, named Lindsay. They lived out in the country, but came in town to school. Harry and I thought we were stuck on them, so one night after supper, when Harry's aunt had gone to sleep, we hitched up Mr. Riker's horse and buggy and drove seven miles out in the country to call on the Lindsay girls. When we got out there it was raining, so we unhitched the horse and put him in the barn and—"

"He got loose, didn't he? And ran all the way home?"

"Yes, but that comes later. We put him in Lindsay's barn and we thought we had him tied all right, and Harry and I went in the house and sat around with the girls. Mrs. Lindsay stayed right in the room with us and did most of the talking—"

"You're sure of that?"

"I certainly am!" She was one of these women that talk all the time. She never stopped. So about half past nine she said the girls would have to go to bed, and that was telling us to get out. Well, to make a long story short, the horse wasn't in the barn and Harry and I walked home seven miles in the pouring rain. We found the horse in his own stall and Harry had to ride him out to Lindsay's next day and get the buggy. That was the last time we ever called on the Lindsay girls."

"Kind of hard on them," said Mrs. Taylor.

"Oh, we were all just kids and there wasn't anything serious between us. Harry's in the insurance business now in Indianapolis, doing fine, he told me."

VI

Louis was almost, but not quite, through with his paper.

"Here's a funny thing," he said. "Although Edinburgh, Scotland, had only 237 ice-cream parlors last season, the number was fifty more than were in the city a year ago."

"I should think that was enough ice-cream parlors."

"Not for the size of the town. Let's see. How big is Edinburgh? I'll have to look it up."

He was on his way to the bookcase when the door-bell rang. He went to the door and admitted Florence Hammond.

"Hello, Louis. Hello, Bess. This isn't a social call. We're out here with a flat tire and Perce wants to borrow your flash."

"There's automobiles for you!" said Louis. "More trouble than they're worth."

"I tried to persuade Perce to take it to the garage and have them fix it, but he's afraid driving it even that far would ruin the rim or the shoe or whatever you call it."

"I'll get the flash and see if I can help him," said Louis.

"And you sit down, Florence, and keep me company," said Mrs. Taylor. "I haven't been out of the house for three days and I'm dying to hear what's going on in Milton."

"You take the Star, don't you?"

"I'm afraid we do, but it hasn't been very thrilling lately."

"You can't blame the paper for that," said Mrs. Hammond. "Nothing exciting has happened; that is, in Milton."

"Has anything happened anywhere?"

"Yes. In Clyde."

"Clyde. That's where your sister lives, isn't it?"

"If you call it living. I'd rather be dead! Honestly, Bess, you and I ought to thank the Lord that we married men who are at least sane and normal. Louis and Perce may not be as good-looking or 'brilliant' as Ed, but anyway we always know where they are and what to expect of them."

"That's true," said Mrs. Taylor.

VII

"I wrote Grace a letter today and told her she was simply crazy not to leave him, especially after this last mess. But she won't give him up. I believe he's got her hypnotized. And she still loves him. She admits his faults and excuses him and expects everybody to do the same. If she didn't, she'd keep her troubles to herself and not write me all the details. I realize everybody has their weakness, but it seems to me there are some things I couldn't forgive. And one of them is a punch in the eye."

"You don't mean—"

"Yes, I do. And Grace took it and accepted his apology when he made one. When I think of it, I simply boil!"

"What was the occasion?"

"No special occasion. Just Saturday night. Everybody in Clyde goes to the Yacht Club Saturday nights. There's no river or lake and no yachts, but they have a sunset gun, so I suppose they're entitled to call it a yacht club. Grace hated it at first and let Ed go alone, but that only made him drink more and get home later Sunday mornings. Besides, she's always been a little jealous, and probably with reason. So she decided to go with him and try to enjoy herself. Grace loves to dance and there are some awfully good dancers in Clyde; that is, early in the evening, before they begin to flounder and reel.

"Of course nobody can say Ed married her under false pretenses. She went into it with her eyes wide open. She saw him for the first time at one of those parties and she fell in love with him when he got mad at a man and knocked him down for cutting in on a dance. The man was about half Ed's size and Ed hit him when he wasn't looking. That didn't make any difference to Grace. And it didn't seem to make any difference to the Yacht Club. Anybody else would have been expelled, but Ed begged everyone's pardon and wasn't even scolded.

"That first night he asked Grace to let him drive her home. She was visiting Helen Morse, and Helen advised her not to take the chance. Ed didn't seem to be in very good driving condition. But Grace was so crazy about him that she told him yes. And then he forgot all about it, went home with another girl and left Grace at the club with some people she hardly knew. She had to call up the Morses and get them to come back after her.

"Well, they met again the next week and Grace thought she would put him in his place by ignoring him entirely, but that didn't work because he didn't remember having seen her before. He was comparatively sober this time and awfully nice and attentive. I'll admit Ed can be nice when he wants to. After that they played tennis together two or three times and then Ed proposed and Grace accepted him and he said he couldn't wait for a big wedding and she agreed to marry him secretly at Colby, a town about thirty miles from Clyde. She was to be in front of the Clyde post-office at twelve o'clock on a certain day and he was to pick her up in his car and drive to Colby and be married.

"The day came and she waited for him an hour and then went back to the Morses'. That evening he telephoned that he had made a mistake in the day and had just discovered it, and would she please forgive him and meet him the next day at the same place. I blush to say she succumbed, though she suspected what she found out later to be true—Ed had been on a bat and was sleeping it off at the time he was supposed to do his eloping.

130

VIII

"They were married and Ed behaved beautifully on the honeymoon. They spent two weeks in New York and went to the theatre every night and sightseeing in the mornings and afternoons. He had men friends of his to dinner once or twice and gave them all they wanted to drink, but wouldn't touch anything himself.

"When they got back to Clyde, Ed bought a lovely house already furnished, and the furniture was just what Grace would have picked out. Grace was so happy it seemed as if it couldn't last, and it didn't.

"They had been in Clyde a week when Ed announced that he had to go away on a trip. He didn't trouble to say where or why or how long. He just went, stayed away five days and came home looking as if he had had five or six operations. Grace tried to get him to tell her where he had been, but he just laughed and said it was a secret.

"And that's the way things have gone on ever since. Ed's got plenty of money and he gives Grace all she can possibly spend, besides buying her presents that are always lovely and terribly expensive. He'll be as good as pie for weeks and weeks—except for the Saturday night carousal—and then he'll disappear for a few days and she won't know where he is or when to expect him home. Her life is one surprise after another. But when he suddenly hits her in the eye, it's more than a surprise. It's a kind of a shock. At least it would be to me."

"When did it happen?" asked Mrs. Taylor.

"A week ago Saturday," said Mrs. Hammond. "There was the usual party at the Yacht Club and Ed took more than his usual amount to drink. Along about midnight he disappeared, and so did a girl named Eva Grayson.

"Finally Grace went home, but she sat up and waited for Ed. He came in about four o'clock pie-eyed. He walked right to where Grace was sitting and without saying anything at all, he hit her, not hard enough to knock her out of her chair but with enough force to really hurt. Then, still not saying anything, he went to bed without taking the time to undress.

"In the morning, or whenever he woke up, he noticed that Grace's eye was discolored and asked her what had happened. She told him and he made no attempt to deny it. All he said was, 'Dearest, I can't tell you how sorry I am. You must believe me when I say I had no idea it was you. I thought it was Eva Grayson. And she deserved to be hit.'

131

IX

"Can you imagine forgiving a man for a thing like that? Can you imagine continuing to live with him and love him? I'd kill myself before I'd stand it! And Grace excuses him and writes me the full details, just as if it were something she was proud of. I tell you, Bess, you and I can consider ourselves lucky—"

The front door opened and Louis came in with his flash-light.

"You're all set, Florence," said he. "I asked Perce in, but he thinks it's time to drive on."

"I know it is," said Mrs. Hammond. "We're going to play bridge out at the Cobbs' and we're terribly late. I ought to have phoned them, but I guess they'll sit up for us. Good night, Bess. I hope I didn't bore you with my long monolog."

"You didn't," said Mrs. Taylor.

X

Louis sat down to finish the Star. Mrs. Taylor shuffled her cards and started a new game, but in the middle of it she rose from the table and went close to her husband's chair.

"Do you know what day this is?" she said.

"Why, yes," Louis replied. "It's Tuesday."

"It's Tuesday, November twelfth. Our anniversary."

"Gosh! That's right! I wish I'd remembered it. I'd have brought you some flowers. Will it do tomorrow?"

"I don't want any flowers. But there is something I would like you to give me. And you don't have to wait till tomorrow."

"What is it?"

"A punch in the eye," said Mrs. Taylor.

"You're feeling kind of funny, aren't you? Did Florence have a shot of their home-made gin in her bag?"

"No. And I'm not feeling funny. I'm just sleepy. I think I'll go to bed."

Louis was reading again.

"It says: 'Experiments in the raising of sisal are being made in Haiti.' I don't suppose you happen to know what sisal is."

But Mrs. Taylor was on her way up-stairs.

Anniversary
Topics for Essays

NOTE. Whichever of these topics you write on and whatever the position you take, remember that your view must rest on an understanding of the details of the story. Your generalizations have to be supported by specific references to the text and by interpretation of those references. Any opinion which is unsupported by evidence is worthless, while any opinion supported by evidence must command respect.

1

Define the vision of life expressed through the story and describe how the sequence, or the character, or the setting, or the situation, or any combination of these elements helps to communicate it.

2

What part in the dramatic structure is played by the visit of the Hammonds?

3

How does Mrs. Taylor feel about her married life, and why?

4

To what extent is Louis conscious of his situation and how important is his consciousness, or lack of it, to the story?

5

Defend or attack the following statement: "Mrs. Taylor's request for a 'punch in the eye' is a good indication of her basic instability."

132

RUDYARD KIPLING   THE MARK OF THE BEAST

I

Your Gods and my Gods
—do you or I know which are the stronger?
Native Proverb

East of Suez, some hold, the direct control of Providence ceases; Man being there handed over to the power of the Gods and Devils of Asia, and the Church of England Providence only exercising an occasional and modified supervision in the case of Englishmen.

This theory accounts for some of the more unnecessary horrors of life in India: it may be stretched to explain my story.

My friend Strickland of the Police, who knows as much of natives of India as is good for any man, can bear witness to the facts of the case. Dumoise, our doctor, also saw what Strickland and I saw. The inference which he drew from the evidence was entirely incorrect. He is dead now; he died in a rather curious manner, which has been elsewhere described.

II

When Fleete came to India he owned a little money and some land in the Himalayas, near a place called Dharmsala. Both properties had been left him by an uncle, and he came out to finance them. He was a big, heavy, genial, and inoffensive man. His knowledge of natives was, of course, limited, and he complained of the difficulties of the language.

He rode in from his place in the hills to spend New Year in the station, and he stayed with Strickland. On New Year's Eve there was a big dinner at the club, and the night was excusably wet. When men foregather from the uttermost ends of the Empire, they have a right to be riotous. The Frontier had sent down a contingent o' Catch-'em-Alive-O's who had not seen twenty white faces for a year, and were used to ride fifteen miles to dinner at the next Fort at the risk of a Khyberee bullet where their drinks should lie. They profited by their new security, for they tried to play pool with a curled-up hedgehog found in the garden, and one of them carried the marker round the room in his teeth. Half a dozen planters had come in from the south and were talking "horse" to the Biggest Liar in Asia, who was trying to cap all their stories at once. Everybody was there, and there was a general closing up of ranks and taking stock of our losses in dead or

disabled that had fallen during the past year. It was a very wet night, and I remember that we sang "Auld Lang Syne" with our feet in the Polo Championship
Cup, and our heads among the stars, and swore that we were all dear friends.
Then some of us went away and annexed Burma, and some tried to open up the
Soudan and were opened up by Fuzzies in that cruel scrub outside Suakim, and
some found stars and medals, and some were married, which was bad, and some
did other things which were worse, and the others of us stayed in our chains and
strove to make money on insufficient experiences.

Fleete began the night with sherry and bitters, drank champagne steadily up to
dessert, then raw, rasping Capri with all the strength of whiskey, took Benedic-
tine with his coffee, four or five whiskies and sodas to improve his pool strokes,
beer and bones at half-past two, winding up with old brandy. Consequently, when
he came out, at half-past three in the morning, into fourteen degrees of frost,
he was very angry with his horse for coughing, and tried to leapfrog into the
saddle. The horse broke away and went to the stables; so Strickland and I formed
a Guard of Dishonour to take Fleete home.

III

Our road lay through the bazaar, close to a little temple of Hanuman, the
Monkey-god, who is a leading divinity worthy of respect. All gods have good
points, just as have all priests. Personally, I attach much importance to Hanuman,
and am kind to his people—the great gray apes of the hills. One never knows
when one may want a friend.

There was a light in the temple, and as we passed we could hear voices of men
chanting hymns. In a native temple the priests rise at all hours of the night to do
honour to their god. Before we could stop him, Fleete dashed up the steps, patted
two priests on the back, and was gravely grinding the ashes of his cigar-butt into
the forehead of the red stone image of Hanuman. Strickland tried to drag him
out, but he sat down and said solemnly:

"Shee that? 'Mark of the B-beasht! I made it. Ishn't it fine?"

In half a minute the temple was alive and noisy, and Strickland, who knew
what came of polluting gods, said that things might occur. He, by virtue of his
official position, long residence in the country, and weakness for going among
the natives, was known to the priests, and he felt unhappy. Fleete sat on the
ground and refused to move. He said that "good old Hanuman" made a very
soft pillow.

Then, without any warning, a Silver Man came out of a recess behind the
image of the god. He was perfectly naked in that bitter, bitter cold, and his body
shone like frosted silver, for he was what the Bible calls "a leper as white as
snow." Also he had no face, because he was a leper of some years' standing, and
his disease was heavy upon him. We two stooped to haul Fleete up, and the
temple was filling and filling with folk who seemed to spring from the earth,
when the Silver Man ran in under our arms, making a noise exactly like the
mewing of an otter, caught Fleete round the body and dropped his head on
Fleete's breast before we could wrench him away. Then he retired to a corner and
sat mewing while the crowd blocked all the doors.

The priests were very angry until the Silver Man touched Fleete. That nuzzling seemed to sober them.

At the end of a few minutes' silence one of the priests came to Strickland and said, in perfect English, "Take your friend away. He has done with Hanuman, but Hanuman has not done with him." The crowd gave room and we carried Fleete into the road.

IV

Strickland was very angry. He said that we might all three have been knifed, and that Fleete should thank his stars that he had escaped without injury.

Fleete thanked no one. He said that he wanted to go to bed. He was gorgeously drunk.

We moved on, Strickland silent and wrathful, until Fleete was taken with violent shivering fits and sweating. He said that the smells of the bazaar were overpowering, and he wondered why slaughterhouses were permitted so near English residences. "Can't you smell the blood?" said Fleete.

We put him to bed at last, just as the dawn was breaking, and Strickland invited me to have another whiskey and soda. While we were drinking he talked of the trouble in the temple, and admitted that it baffled him completely. Strickland hates being mystified by natives, because his business in life is to overmatch them with their own weapons. He has not yet succeeded in doing this, but in fifteen or twenty years he will have made some small progress.

"They should have mauled us," he said, "instead of mewing at us. I wonder what they meant. I don't like it one little bit."

I said that the Managing Committee of the temple would in all probability bring a criminal action against us for insulting their religion. There was a section of the Indian Penal Code which exactly met Fleete's offence. Strickland said he only hoped and prayed that they would do this. Before I left I looked into Fleete's room, and saw him lying on his right side, scratching his left breast. Then I went to bed, cold, depressed, and unhappy at seven o'clock in the morning.

V

At one o'clock I rode over to Strickland's house to inquire after Fleete's head. I imagined that it would be a sore one. Fleete was breakfasting and seemed unwell. His temper was gone, for he was abusing the cook for not supplying him with an underdone chop. A man who can eat raw meat after a wet night is a curiosity. I told Fleete this, and he laughed.

"You breed queer mosquitos in these parts," he said. "I've been bitten to pieces, but only in one place."

"Let's have a look at the bite," said Strickland. "It may have gone down since this morning."

While the chops were being cooked, Fleete opened his shirt and showed us, just over his left breast, a mark, the perfect double of the black rosettes—the five or six irregular blotches arranged in a circle—on a leopard's hide. Strickland looked and said, "It was only pink this morning. It's grown black now."

Fleete ran to a glass.

135

"By Jove!" he said, "this is nasty. What is it?"

We could not answer. Here the chops came in, all red and juicy, and Fleete bolted three in a most offensive manner. He ate on his right grinders only, and threw his head over his right shoulder as he snapped the meat. When he had finished, it struck him that he had been behaving strangely, for he said apologetically, "I don't think I ever felt so hungry in my life. I've bolted like an ostrich."

After breakfast Strickland said to me, "Don't go. Stay here, and stay for the night."

136

Seeing that my house was not three miles from Strickland's, this request was absurd. But Strickland insisted, and was going to say something when Fleete interrupted by declaring in a shame-faced way that he felt hungry again. Strickland sent a man to my house to fetch over my bedding and a horse, and we three went down to Strickland's stables to pass the hours until it was time to go out for a ride. The man who has a weakness for horses never wearies of inspecting them; and when two men are killing time in this way they gather knowledge and lies the one from the other.

There were five horses in the stables, and I shall never forget the scene as we tried to look them over. They seemed to have gone mad. They reared and screamed and nearly tore up their pickets; they sweated and shivered and lathered and were distraught with fear. Strickland's horses used to know him as well as his dogs; which made the matter more curious. We left the stable for fear of the brutes throwing themselves in their panic. Then Strickland turned back and called me. The horses were still frightened, but they let us "gentle" and make much of them, and put their heads in our bosoms.

"They aren't afraid of *us*," said Strickland. "D'you know, I'd give three months' pay if Outrage here could talk."

But Outrage was dumb, and could only cuddle up to his master and blow out his nostrils, as is the custom of horses when they wish to explain things but can't. Fleete came up when we were in the stalls, and as soon as the horses saw him their fright broke out afresh. It was all that we could do to escape from the place unkicked. Strickland said, "They don't seem to love you, Fleete."

"Nonsense," said Fleete; "my mare will follow me like a dog." He went to her; she was in a loose-box; but as he slipped the bars she plunged, knocked him down, and broke away into the garden. I laughed, but Strickland was not amused. He took his moustache in both fists and pulled at it till it nearly came out. Fleete, instead of going off to chase his property, yawned, saying that he felt sleepy. He went to the house to lie down, which was a foolish way of spending New Year's Day.

VI

Strickland sat with me in the stables and asked if I had noticed anything peculiar in Fleete's manner. I said that he ate his food like a beast; but that this might have been the result of living alone in the hills out of the reach of society as refined and elevating as ours, for instance. Strickland was not amused. I do not think that he listened to me, for his next sentence referred to the mark on Fleete's breast, and I said that it might have been caused by blisterflies, or that it was possibly a birth-mark newly born and now visible for the first time. We both agreed that it was unpleasant to look at, and Strickland found occasion to say that I was a fool.

"I can't tell you what I think now," said he, "because you would call me a madman; but you must stay with me for the next few days, if you can. I want you to watch Fleete, but don't tell me what you think till I have made up my mind."

"But I am dining out to-night," I said.

"So am I," said Strickland, "and so is Fleete. At least if he doesn't change his mind."

We walked about the garden smoking, but saying nothing—because we were friends, and talking spoils good tobacco—till our pipes were out. Then we went to wake up Fleete. He was wide awake and fidgeting about his room.

"I say, I want some more chops," he said. "Can I get them?"

We laughed and said, "Go and change. The ponies will be round in a minute."

"All right," said Fleete. "I'll go when I get the chops—underdone ones, mind."

He seemed to be quite in earnest. It was four o'clock, and we had had breakfast at one; still, for a long time, he demanded those underdone chops. Then he changed into riding clothes and went out into the verandah. His pony—the mare had not been caught—would not let him come near. All three horses were unmanageable—mad with fear—and finally Fleete said that he would stay at home and get something to eat. Strickland and I rode out wondering. As we passed the temple of Hanuman, the Silver Man came out and mewed at us.

"He is not one of the regular priests of the temple," said Strickland. "I think I should peculiarly like to lay my hands on him."

There was no spring in our gallop on the racecourse that evening. The horses were stale, and moved as though they had been ridden out.

"The fright after breakfast has been too much for them," said Strickland.

That was the only remark he made through the remainder of the ride. Once or twice I think he swore to himself; but that did not count.

VII

We came back in the dark at seven o'clock, and saw that there were no lights in the bungalow. "Careless ruffians my servants are!" said Strickland.

My horse reared at something on the carriage-drive, and Fleete stood up under its nose.

"What are you doing, grovelling about the garden?" said Strickland.

But both horses bolted and nearly threw us. We dismounted by the stables and returned to Fleete, who was on his hands and knees under the orange-bushes.

"What the devil's wrong with you?" said Strickland.

"Nothing, nothing in the world," said Fleete, speaking very quickly and thickly. "I've been gardening—botanising, you know. The smell of the earth is delightful. I think I'm going for a walk—a long walk—all night."

Then I saw that there was something excessively out of order somewhere, and I said to Strickland, "I am not dining out."

"Bless you!" said Strickland. "Here, Fleete, get up. You'll catch fever there. Come in to dinner and let's have the lamps lit. We'll all dine at home."

Fleete stood up unwillingly, and said, "No lamps—no lamps. It's much nicer here. Let's dine outside and have some more chops—lots of 'em and underdone—bloody ones with gristle."

Now a December evening in Northern India is bitterly cold, and Fleete's suggestion was that of a maniac.

"Come in," said Strickland sternly. "Come in at once."

Fleete came, and when the lamps were brought, we saw that he was literally plastered with dirt from head to foot. He must have been rolling in the garden. He shrank from the light and went to his room. His eyes were horrible to look at. There was a green light behind them, not in them, if you understand, and the man's lower lip hung down.

Strickland said, "There is going to be trouble—big trouble—to-night. Don't you change your riding-things."

VIII

We waited and waited for Fleete's reappearance, and ordered dinner in the meantime. We could hear him moving about his own room, but there was no light there. Presently from the room came the long-drawn howl of a wolf.

People write and talk lightly of blood running cold and hair standing up and things of that kind. Both sensations are too horrible to be trifled with. My heart stopped as though a knife had been driven through it, and Strickland turned as white as the tablecloth.

The howl was repeated, and was answered by another howl far across the fields.

That set the gilded roof on the horror. Strickland dashed into Fleete's room. I followed, and we saw Fleete getting out of the window. He made beast-noises in the back of his throat. He could not answer us when we shouted at him. He spat.

I don't quite remember what followed, but I think that Strickland must have stunned him with the long boot-jack or else I should never have been able to sit on his chest. Fleete could not speak, he could only snarl, and his snarls were those of a wolf, not of a man. The human spirit must have been giving way all day and have died out with the twilight. We were dealing with a beast that had once been Fleete.

The affair was beyond any human and rational experience. I tried to say "Hydrophobia," but the word wouldn't come, because I knew that I was lying.

We bound this beast with leather thongs of the punkah-rope, and tied its thumbs and big toes together, and gagged it with a shoe-horn, which makes a very efficient gag if you know how to arrange it. Then we carried it into the dining-room, and sent a man to Dumoise, the doctor, telling him to come over at once. After we had despatched the messenger and were drawing breath, Strickland said, "It's no good. This isn't any doctor's work." I, also, knew that he spoke the truth.

The beast's head was free, and it threw it about from side to side. Any one entering the room would have believed that we were curing a wolf's pelt. That was the most loathsome accessory of all.

Strickland sat with his chin in the heel of his fist, watching the beast as it wriggled on the ground, but saying nothing. The shirt had been torn open in the scuffle and showed the black rosette mark on the left breast. It stood out like a blister.

In the silence of the watching we heard something without mewing like a she-otter. We both rose to our feet, and, I answer for myself, not Strickland, felt sick —actually and physically sick. We told each other, as did the men in "Pinafore," that it was the cat.

139

IX

Dumoise arrived, and I never saw a little man so unprofessionally shocked. He said that it was a heart-rending case of hydrophobia, and that nothing could be done. At least any palliative measures would only prolong the agony. The beast was foaming at the mouth. Fleete, as we told Dumoise, had been bitten by dogs once or twice. Any man who keeps half a dozen terriers must expect a nip now and again. Dumoise could offer no help. He could only certify that Fleete was dying of hydrophobia. The beast was then howling, for it had managed to spit out the shoehorn. Dumoise said that he would be ready to certify to the cause of death, and that the end was certain. He was a good little man, and he offered to remain with us; but Strickland refused the kindness. He did not wish to poison Dumoise's New Year. He would only ask him not give the real cause of Fleete's death to the public.

X

So Dumoise left, deeply agitated; and as soon as the noise of the cart-wheels had died away, Strickland told me, in a whisper, his suspicions. They were so wildly improbable that he dared not say them out aloud; and I, who entertained all Strickland's beliefs, was so ashamed of owning to them that I pretended to disbelieve.

"Even if the Silver Man had bewitched Fleete for polluting the image of Hanu-man, the punishment could not have fallen so quickly."

As I was whispering this the cry outside the house rose again, and the beast fell into a fresh paroxysm of struggling till we were afraid that the thongs that held it would give way.

"Watch!" said Strickland. "If this happens six times I shall take the law into my own hands. I order you to help me."

He went into his room and came out in a few minutes with the barrels of an old shot-gun, a piece of fishing-line, some thick cord, and his heavy wooden bedstead. I reported that the convulsions had followed the cry by two seconds in each case, and the beast seemed perceptibly weaker.

Strickland muttered, "But he can't take away the life! He can't take away the life!"

I said, though I knew that I was arguing against myself, "It may be a cat. It must be a cat. If the Silver Man is responsible, why does he dare to come here?"

Strickland arranged the wood on the hearth, put the gun-barrels into the glow of the fire, spread the twine on the table, and broke a walking-stick in two. There was one yard of fishing-line, gut, lapped with wire, such as is used for *mahseer-fishing*, and he tied the two ends together in a loop.

Then he said, "How can we catch him? He must be taken alive and unhurt."

I said that we must trust in Providence, and go out softly with polo-sticks into the shrubbery at the front of the house. The man or animal that made the cry was evidently moving round the house as regularly as a night watchman. We could wait in the bushes till he came by, and knock him over.

Strickland accepted this suggestion, and we slipped out from a bath-room window into the front verandah and then across the carriage-drive into the bushes.

In the moonlight we could see the leper coming round the corner of the house. He was perfectly naked, and from time to time he mewed and stopped to dance with his shadow. It was an unattractive sight, and thinking of poor Fleete, brought to such degradation by so foul a creature, I put away all my doubts and resolved to help Strickland from the heated gun-barrels to the loop of twine— from the loins to the head and back again—with all tortures that might be needful.

The leper halted in the front porch for a moment and we jumped out on him with the sticks. He was wonderfully strong, and we were afraid that he might escape or be fatally injured before we caught him. We had an idea that lepers were frail creatures, but this proved to be incorrect. Strickland knocked his legs from ūnder him, and I put my foot on his neck. He mewed hideously, and even through my riding-boots I could feel that his flesh was not the flesh of a clean man.

He struck at us with his hand and feet-stumps. We looped the lash of a dog-whip round him, under the arm-pits, and dragged him backwards into the hall and so into the dining-room where the beast lay. There we tied him with trunk-straps. He made no attempt to escape, but mewed.

XI

When we confronted him with the beast the scene was beyond description. The beast doubled backwards into a bow, as though he had been poisoned with strychnine, and moaned in the most pitiable fashion. Several other things happened also, but they cannot be put down here.

"I think I was right," said Strickland. "Now we will ask him to cure this case."

But the leper only mewed. Strickland wrapped a towel round his hand and took the gun-barrels out of the fire. I put the half of the broken walking-stick through a loop of fishing-line and buckled the leper comfortably to Strickland's bedstead. I understood then how men and women and little children can endure to see a witch burnt alive; for the beast was moaning on the floor, and though the Silver Man had no face, you could see horrible feelings passing through the slab that took its place, exactly as waves of heat play across red-hot iron—gun-barrels for instance.

Strickland shaded his eyes with his hands for a moment, and we got to work. This part is not to be printed.

The dawn was beginning to break when the leper spoke. His mewings had not been satisfactory up to that point. The beast had fainted from exhaustion, and the house was very still. We unstrapped the leper and told him to take away the evil spirit. He crawled to the beast and laid his hand upon the left breast. That was all. Then he fell face down and whined, drawing in his breath as he did so.

We watched the face of the beast, and saw the soul of Fleete coming back into the eyes. Then a sweat broke out on the forehead, and the eyes—they were human eyes—closed. We waited for an hour, but Fleete still slept. We carried him to his room and bade the leper go, giving him the bedstead, and the sheet on the bedstead to cover his nakedness, the gloves and the towels with which we had touched him, and the whip that had been hooked round his body. He put the sheet about him and went out into the early morning without speaking or mewing.

XII

Strickland wiped his face and sat down. A night-gong, far away in the city, made seven o'clock.

"Exactly four-and-twenty hours!" said Strickland. "And I've done enough to ensure my dismissal from the service, besides permanent quarters in a lunatic asylum. Do you believe that we are awake?"

The red-hot gun-barrel had fallen on the floor and was singeing the carpet. The smell was entirely real.

That morning at eleven we two together went to wake up Fleete. We looked and saw that the black leopard-rosette on his chest had disappeared. He was very drowsy and tired, but as soon as he saw us, he said, "Oh! Confound you fellows. Happy New Year to you. Never mix your liquors. I'm nearly dead."

"Thanks for your kindness, but you're over time," said Strickland. "To-day is the morning of the second. You've slept the clock round with a vengeance."

The door opened, and little Dumoise put his head in. He had come on foot, and fancied that we were laying out Fleete.

"I've brought a nurse," said Dumoise. "I suppose that she can come in for . . . what is necessary."

"By all means," said Fleete cheerily, sitting up in bed. "Bring on your nurses."

Dumoise was dumb. Strickland led him out and explained that there must have been a mistake in the diagnosis. Dumoise remained dumb and left the house hastily. He considered that his professional reputation had been injured, and was inclined to make a personal matter of the recovery. Strickland went out too. When he came back, he said that he had been to call on the temple of Hanuman to offer redress for the pollution of the god, and had been solemnly assured that no white man had ever touched the idol, and that he was an incarnation of all the virtues laboring under a delusion. "What do you think?" said Strickland.

I said, "There are more things . . ."

The Mark of the Beast
Topics for Essays

NOTE. Whichever of these topics you write on and whatever the position you take, remember that your view must rest on an understanding of the details of the story. Your generalizations have to be supported by specific references to the text and by interpretation of those references. Any opinion which is unsupported by evidence is worthless, while any opinion supported by evidence must command respect.

1

Define the vision of life expressed through the story and describe how the sequence, or the character, or the setting, or the situation, or any combination of these elements helps to communicate it.

2

Why does Fleete's character make it peculiarly appropriate that he should be the one to undergo this experience?

3

Show how the treatment of the leper at the hands of Strickland and the narrator suggest something about their relationship to "the beast"? Define the attitudes of Strickland and the narrator toward "the beast."

4

Examine the vision this story reveals about the relationship of man to the supernatural.

5

Examine what the story reveals about the relationships of colonial rulers and administrators to the natives of the colonized country.

6

Defend or attack the following statement: "The story dramatizes the idea that no man, 'civilized' or not, can escape the mark of the beast."

PART FOUR   STORIES FOR FURTHER STUDY

The ten stories in this section are presented in their original form. We have   143
not broken them into sections,* nor are there questions to help you organize the
details into your own imaginative construction of the writer's vision. From here
on, you are on your own.

And, of course, this is as it should be. The purpose of this text was to help you
discipline your imagination in order to become a more proficient reader of fiction.
If you have followed the instructions up to now, you should have begun to
develop an eye for details, a sense of structure, an awareness of setting, char-
acterization, situation and action, all of which should lead you to a more specific,
concrete awareness of the vision the story presents. In reading the following ten
stories you should be able to put into practice the disciplined imagination we have
tried to help you develop.

Your instructor may ask you to break some of these stories into appropriate
sections, and to prepare, for class discussion, questions and answers dealing
with specific details of setting, situation, character, or other elements. But even
while doing this, you should keep in mind that such exercises are only means
to an end—that end being the understanding and awareness that come into
being when the disciplined imagination is actively engaged in creating a vision
of life from the details of fiction. The ultimate reward which the disciplined
imagination brings to its possessor is this ability to enter into the worlds of
fiction, to participate in the various experiences these worlds provide, and to
emerge with a clearer perception of life.

We hope we have helped you toward this end. Good luck, and good reading
from here on.

---

*
You may notice that some of the stories in this part
are divided into sections. These divisions are the
authors', not ours.

144   It was mid-morning—a very cold, bright day. Holding a potted plant before her, a girl of fourteen jumped off the bus in front of the Old Ladies' Home, on the outskirts of town. She wore a red coat, and her straight yellow hair was hanging down loose from the pointed white cap all the little girls were wearing that year. She stopped for a moment beside one of the prickly dark shrubs with which the city had beautified the Home, and then proceeded slowly toward the building, which was of whitewashed brick and reflected the winter sunlight like a block of ice. As she walked vaguely up the steps she shifted the small pot from hand to hand; then she had to set it down and remove her mittens before she could open the heavy door.

"I'm a Campfire Girl. . . . I have to pay a visit to some old lady," she told the nurse at the desk. This was a woman in a white uniform who looked as if she were cold; she had close-cut hair which stood up on the very top of her head exactly like a sea wave. Marian, the little girl, did not tell her that this visit would give her a minimum of only three points in her score.

"Acquainted with any of our residents?" asked the nurse. She lifted one eyebrow and spoke like a man.

"With any old ladies? No—but—that is, any of them will do," Marian stammered. With her free hand she pushed her hair behind her ears, as she did when it was time to study Science.

The nurse shrugged and rose. "You have a nice *multiflora cineraria* there," she remarked as she walked ahead down the hall of closed doors to pick out an old lady.

There was loose, bulging linoleum on the floor. Marian felt as if she were walking on the waves, but the nurse paid no attention to it. There was a smell in the hall like the interior of a clock. Everything was silent until, behind one of the doors, an old lady of some kind cleared her throat like a sheep bleating. This decided the nurse. Stopping in her tracks, she first extended her arm, bent her elbow, and leaned forward from the hips—all to examine the watch strapped to her wrist; then she gave a loud double-rap on the door.

"There are two in each room," the nurse remarked over her shoulder.

"Two what?" asked Marian without thinking. The sound like a sheep's bleating almost made her turn around and run back.

One old woman was pulling the door open in short, gradual jerks, and when she saw the nurse a strange smile forced her old face dangerously awry. Marian, suddenly propelled by the strong, impatient arm of the nurse, saw next the side-face of another old woman, even older, who was lying flat in bed with a cap on and a counterpane drawn up to her chin.

"Visitor," said the nurse, and after one more shove she was off up the hall.

Marian stood tongue-tied; both hands held the potted plant. The old woman, still with that terrible, square smile (which was a smile of welcome) stamped on her bony face, was waiting. . . . Perhaps she said something. The old woman in bed said nothing at all, and she did not look around.

145

Suddenly Marian saw a hand, quick as a bird claw, reach up in the air and pluck the white cap off her head. At the same time, another claw to match drew her all the way into the room, and the next moment the door closed behind her.

"My, my, my," said the old lady at her side.

Marian stood enclosed by a bed, a washstand, and a chair; the tiny room had altogether too much furniture. Everything smelled wet—even the bare floor. She held onto the back of the chair, which was wicker and felt soft and damp. Her heart beat more and more slowly, her hands got colder and colder, and she could not hear whether the old women were saying anything or not. She could not see them very clearly. How dark it was! The window shade was down, and the only door was shut. Marian looked at the ceiling. . . . It was like being caught in a robber's cave, just before one was murdered.

"Did you come to be our little girl for a while?" the first robber asked.

Then something was snatched from Marian's hand—the little potted plant.

"Flowers!" screamed the old woman. She stood holding the pot in an undecided way. "Pretty flowers," she added.

Then the old woman in bed cleared her throat and spoke. "They are not pretty," she said, still without looking around, but very distinctly.

Marian suddenly pitched against the chair and sat down in it.

"Pretty flowers," the first old woman insisted. "Pretty—pretty. . . ."

Marian wished she had the little pot back for just a moment—she had forgotten to look at the plant herself before giving it away. What did it look like?

"Stinkweeds," said the other old woman sharply. She had a bunchy white forehead and red eyes like a sheep. Now she turned them toward Marian. The fogginess seemed to rise in her throat again, and she bleated, "Who—are—you?"

To her suprise, Marian could not remember her name. "I'm a Campfire Girl," she said finally.

"Watch out for the germs," said the old woman like a sheep, not addressing anyone.

"One came out last month to see us," said the first old woman.

A sheep or a germ? wondered Marian dreamily, holding onto the chair.

"Did not!" cried the other old woman.

"Did so! Read to us out of the Bible, and we enjoyed it!" screamed the first.

"Who enjoyed it!" said the woman in bed. Her mouth was unexpectedly small and sorrowful, like a pet's.

"We enjoyed it," insisted the other. "You enjoyed it—I enjoyed it."

"We all enjoyed it," said Marian, without realizing that she had said a word.

The first old woman had just finished putting the potted plant high, high on the top of the wardrobe, where it could hardly be seen from below. Marian wondered how she had ever succeeded in placing it there, how she could ever have reached so high.

"You mustn't pay any attention to old Addie," she now said to the little girl. "She's ailing today."

"Will you shut your mouth?" said the woman in bed. "I am not."

"You're a story."

"I can't stay but a minute—really, I can't," said Marian suddenly. She looked down at the wet floor and thought that if she were sick in here they would have to let her go.

With much to-do the first old woman sat down in a rocking chair—still another piece of furniture!—and began to rock. With the fingers of one hand she touched a very dirty cameo pin on her chest. "What do you do at school?" she asked.

"I don't know . . ." said Marian. She tried to think but she could not.

"Oh, but the flowers are beautiful," the old woman whispered. She seemed to rock faster and faster; Marian did not see how anyone could rock so fast.

"Ugly," said the woman in bed.

"If we bring flowers—" Marian began, and then fell silent. She had almost said that if Campfire Girls brought flowers to the Old Ladies' Home, the visit would count one extra point, and if they took a Bible with them on the bus and read it to the old ladies, it counted double. But the old woman had not listened, anyway; she was rocking and watching the other one, who watched back from the bed.

"Poor Addie is ailing. She has to take medicine—see?" she said, pointing a horny finger at a row of bottles on the table, and rocking so high that her black comfort shoes lifted off the floor like a little child's.

"I am no more sick that you are," said the woman in bed.

"Oh yes you are!"

"I just got more sense than you have, that's all," said the other old woman, nodding her head.

"That's only the contrary way she talks when *you all* come," said the first old lady with sudden intimacy. She stopped the rocker with a neat pat of her feet and leaned toward Marian. Her hand reached over—it felt like a petunia leaf, clinging and just a little sticky.

"Will you hush! Will you hush!" cried the other one.

Marian leaned back rigidly in her chair.

"When I was a little girl like you, I went to school and all," said the old woman in the same intimate, menacing voice. "Not here—another town. . . ."

"Hush!" said the sick woman. "You never went to school. You never came and you never went. You never were anywhere—only here. You never were born! You don't know anything. Your head is empty, your heart and hands and your old black purse are all empty, even that little old box that you brought with you, you brought empty—you showed it to me. And yet you talk, talk, talk, talk, talk all the time until I think I'm losing my mind. Who are you? You're a stranger—a perfect stranger! Don't you know you're a stranger? Is it possible that they have actually done a thing like this to anyone—sent them in a stranger to talk, and rock, and tell away her whole long rigmarole? Do they seriously suppose that I'll be able to keep it up, day in, day out, night in, night out, living in the same room with a terrible old woman—forever?"

Marian saw the old woman's eyes grow bright and turn toward her. This old woman was looking at her with despair and calculation in her face. Her small lips suddenly dropped apart, and exposed a half circle of false teeth with tan gums.

"Come here, I want to tell you something," she whispered. "Come here!"

Marian was trembling, and her heart nearly stopped beating altogether for a moment.

"Now, now, Addie," said the first old woman. "That's not polite. Do you know what's really the matter with old Addie today?" She, too, looked at Marian; one of her eyelids drooped low.

"The matter?" the child repeated stupidly. "What's the matter with her?"

"Why, she's mad because it's her birthday!" said the first old woman, beginning to rock again and giving a little crow as though she had answered her own riddle.

"It is not, it is not!" screamed the old woman in bed. "It is not my birthday, no one knows when that is but myself, and will you please be quiet and say nothing more, or I'll go straight out of my mind!" She turned her eyes toward Marian again, and presently she said in the soft, foggy voice, "When the worst comes to the worst, I ring this bell, and the nurse comes." One of her hands was drawn out from under the patched counterpane—a thin little hand with enormous black freckles. With a finger which would not hold still she pointed to a little bell on the table among the bottles.

"How old are you?" Marian breathed. Now she could see the old woman in bed very closely and plainly, and very abruptly, from all sides, as in dreams. She wondered about her—she wondered for a moment as though there was nothing else in the world to wonder about. It was the first time such a thing had happened to Marian.

"I won't tell!"

The old face on the pillow, where Marian was bending over it, slowly gathered and collapsed. Soft whimpers came out of the small open mouth. It was a sheep that she sounded like—a little lamb. Marian's face drew very close, the yellow hair hung forward.

"She's crying!" She turned a bright, burning face up to the first old woman.

"That's Addie for you," the old woman said spitefully.

Marian jumped up and moved toward the door. For the second time, the claw almost touched her hair, but it was not quick enough. The little girl put her cap on.

"Well, it was a real visit," said the old woman, following Marian through the doorway and all the way out into the hall. Then from behind she suddenly clutched the child with her sharp little fingers. In an affected, high-pitched whine she cried, "Oh, little girl, have you a penny to spare for a poor old woman that's not got anything of her own? We don't have a thing in the world—not a penny for candy—not a thing! Little girl, just a nickel—a penny—"

Marian pulled violently against the old hands for a moment before she was free. Then she ran down the hall, without looking behind her and without looking at the nurse, who was reading *Field & Stream* at her desk. The nurse, after another triple motion to consult her wrist watch, asked automatically the question put to visitors in all institutions: "Won't you stay and have dinner with *us?*"

Marian never replied. She pushed the heavy door open into the cold air and ran down the steps.

Under the prickly shrub she stopped and quickly, without being seen, retrieved a red apple she had hidden there.

Her yellow hair under the white cap, her scarlet coat, her bare knees all flashed in the sunlight as she ran to meet the big bus rocketing through the street.

"Wait for me!" she shouted. As though at an imperial command, the bus ground to a stop.

She jumped on and took a big bite out of the apple.

148

D. H. LAWRENCE   THE ROCKING-HORSE WINNER

There was a woman who was beautiful, who started with all the advantages,
yet she had no luck. She married for love, and the love turned to dust. She had
bonny children, yet she felt they had been thrust upon her, and she could not
love them. They looked at her coldly, as if they were finding fault with her. And
hurriedly she felt she must cover up some fault in herself. Yet what it was that
she must cover up she never knew. Nevertheless, when her children were
present, she always felt the centre of her heart go hard. This troubled her, and
in her manner she was all the more gentle and anxious for her children, as if
she loved them very much. Only she herself knew that at the centre of her heart
was a hard little place that could not feel love, no, not for anybody. Everybody
else said of her: "She is such a good mother. She adores her children." Only she
herself, and her children themselves, knew it was not so. They read it in each
other's eyes.

There were a boy and two little girls. They lived in a pleasant house, with a
garden, and they had discreet servants, and felt themselves superior to anyone
in the neighbourhood.

Although they lived in style, they felt always an anxiety in the house. There
was never enough money. The mother had a small income, and the father had
a small income, but not nearly enough for the social position which they had to
keep up. The father went into town to some office. But though he had good
prospects, these prospects never materialized. There was always the grinding
sense of the shortage of money, though the style was always kept up.

At last the mother said: "I will see if I can't make something." But she did
not know where to begin. She racked her brains, and tried this thing and the
other, but could not find anything successful. The failure made deep lines come
into her face. Her children were growing up, they would have to go to school.
There must be more money, there must be more money. The father, who was always very handsome and expensive in his tastes, seemed as if he never would

*

From *The Complete Short Stories*, Vol. III of D. H.
Lawrence. Copyright 1933 by the estate of D. H.
Lawrence, © 1961 by Angelo Ravagli and C. Mon-
tague Weekley, Executors of the Estate of Frieda
Lawrence Ravagli. Reprinted by permission of The
Viking Press, Inc.

be able to do anything worth doing. And the mother, who had a great belief in herself, did not succeed any better, and her tastes were just as expensive.

And so the house came to be haunted by the unspoken phrase: There must be more money! There must be more money! The children could hear it all the time, though nobody said it aloud. They heard it at Christmas, when the expensive and splendid toys filled the nursery. Behind the shining modern rocking horse, behind the smart doll's-house, a voice would start whispering: "There must be more money! There must be more money!" And the children would stop playing, to listen for a moment. They would look into each other's eyes, to see if they had all heard. And each one saw in the eyes of the other two that they too had heard. "There must be more money! There must be more money!"

It came whispering from the springs of the still-swaying rocking horse, and even the horse, bending his wooden, champing head, heard it. The big doll, sitting so pink and smirking in her new pram, could hear it quite plainly, and seemed to be smirking all the more self-consciously because of it. The foolish puppy, too, that took the place of the Teddy bear, he was looking so extraordinarily foolish for no other reason but that he heard the secret whisper all over the house: "There must be more money!"

Yet nobody ever said it aloud. The whisper was everywhere, and therefore no one spoke it. Just as no one ever says: "We are breathing!" in spite of the fact that breath is coming and going all the time.

"Mother," said the boy Paul one day, "why don't we keep a car of our own? Why do we always use uncle's, or else a taxi?"

"Because we're the poor members of the family," said the mother.

"But why are we, mother?"

"Well—I suppose," she said slowly and bitterly, "it's because your father has no luck."

The boy was silent for some time.

"Is luck money, mother?" he asked, rather timidly.

"No, Paul. Not quite. It's what causes you to have money."

"Oh!" said Paul vaguely. "I thought when Uncle Oscar said filthy lucker, it meant money."

"Filthy lucre does mean money," said the mother. "But it's lucre, not luck."

"Oh!" said the boy. "Then what is luck, mother?"

"It's what causes you to have money. If you're lucky you have money. That's why it's better to be born lucky than rich. If you're rich, you may lose your money. But if you're lucky, you will always get more money."

"Oh! Will you? And is father not lucky?"

"Very unlucky, I should say," she said bitterly.

The boy watched her with unsure eyes.

"Why?" he asked.

"I don't know. Nobody ever knows why one person is lucky and another unlucky."

"Don't they? Nobody at all? Does nobody know?"

"Perhaps God. But He never tells."

"He ought to, then. And aren't you lucky either, mother?"

"I can't be, if I married an unlucky husband."

"But by yourself, aren't you?"

"I used to think I was, before I married. Now I think I am very unlucky indeed."

"Why?"

"Well—never mind! Perhaps I'm not really," she said.

The child looked at her, to see if she meant it. But he saw, by the lines of her mouth, that she was only trying to hide something from him.

"Well, anyhow," he said stoutly, "I'm a lucky person."

"Why?" said his mother, with a sudden laugh.

He stared at her. He didn't even know why he had said it.

"God told me," he asserted, brazening it out.

"I hope He did, dear!" she said, again with a laugh, but rather bitter.

"He did, mother!"

"Excellent!" said the mother, using one of her husband's exclamations.

The boy saw she did not believe him; or, rather, that she paid no attention to his assertion. This angered him somewhat, and made him want to compel her attention.

He went off by himself, vaguely, in a childish way, seeking for the clue to "luck." Absorbed, taking no heed of other people, he went about with a sort of stealth, seeking inwardly for luck. He wanted luck, he wanted it, he wanted it. When the two girls were playing dolls in the nursery, he would sit on his big rocking horse, charging madly into space, with a frenzy that made the little girls peer at him uneasily. Wildly the horse careered, the waving dark hair of the boy tossed, his eyes had a strange glare in them. The little girls dared not speak to him.

When he had ridden to the end of his mad little journey, he climbed down and stood in front of his rocking horse, staring fixedly into its lowered face. Its red mouth was slightly open, its big eye was wide and glassy-bright.

"Now!" he would silently command the snorting steed. "Now, take me to where there is luck! Now take me!"

And he would slash the horse on the neck with the little whip he had asked Uncle Oscar for. He knew the horse could take him to where there was luck, if only he forced it. So he would mount again, and start on his furious ride, hoping at last to get there. He knew he could get there.

"You'll break your horse, Paul!" said the nurse.

"He's always riding like that! I wish he'd leave off!" said his elder sister Joan.

But he only glared down on them in silence. Nurse gave him up. She could make nothing of him. Anyhow he was growing beyond her.

One day his mother and his Uncle Oscar came in when he was on one of his furious rides. He did not speak to them.

"Hallo, you young jockey! Riding a winner?" said his uncle.

"Aren't you growing too big for a rocking horse? You're not a very little boy any longer, you know," said his mother.

151

But Paul only gave a blue glare from his big, rather close-set eyes. He would speak to nobody when he was in full tilt. His mother watched him with an anxious expression on her face.

At last he suddenly stopped forcing his horse into the mechanical gallop, and slid down.

"Well, I got there!" he announced fiercely, his blue eyes still flaring, and his sturdy long legs straddling apart.

"Where did you get to?" asked his mother.

"Where I wanted to go," he flared back at her.

"That's right, son!" said Uncle Oscar. "Don't you stop till you get there. What's the horse's name?"

"He doesn't have a name," said the boy.

"Gets on without all right?" asked the uncle.

"Well, he has different names. He was called Sansovino last week."

"Sansovino, eh? Won the Ascot. How did you know his name?"

"He always talks about horse races with Bassett," said Joan.

The uncle was delighted to find that his small nephew was posted with all the racing news. Bassett, the young gardener, who had been wounded in the left foot in the war and had got his present job through Oscar Cresswell, whose batman he had been, was a perfect blade of the "turf." He lived in the racing events, and the small boy lived with him.

Oscar Cresswell got it all from Bassett.

"Master Paul comes and asks me, so I can't do more than tell him, sir," said Bassett, his face terribly serious, as if he were speaking of religious matters.

"And does he ever put anything on a horse he fancies?"

"Well—I don't want to give him away—he's a young sport, a fine sport, sir. Would you mind asking him yourself? He sort of takes a pleasure in it, and perhaps he'd feel I was giving him away, sir, if you don't mind."

Bassett was serious as a church.

The uncle went back to his nephew, and took him off for a ride in the car.

"Say, Paul, old man, do you ever put anything on a horse?" the uncle asked.

The boy watched the handsome man closely.

"Why, do you think I oughtn't to?" he parried.

"Not a bit of it! I thought perhaps you might give me a tip for the Lincoln."

The car sped on into the country, going down to Uncle Oscar's place in Hampshire.

"Honour bright?" said the nephew.

"Honour bright, son!" said the uncle.

"Well, then, Daffodil."

"Daffodil! I doubt it, sonny. What about Mirza?"

"I only know the winner," said the boy. "That's Daffodil."

"Daffodil, eh?"

There was a pause. Daffodil was an obscure horse comparatively.

"Uncle!"

"Yes, son?"

"You won't let it go any further, will you? I promised Bassett."

"Bassett be damned, old man! What's he got to do with it?"

"We're partners. We've been partners from the first. Uncle, he lent me my first five shillings, which I lost. I promised him, honour bright, it was only between me and him; only you gave me that ten-shilling note I started winning with, so I thought you were lucky. You won't let it go any further, will you?"

The boy gazed at his uncle from those big, hot, blue eyes, set rather close together. The uncle stirred and laughed uneasily.

"Right you are, son! I'll keep your tip private. Daffodil, eh? How much are you putting on him?"

"All except twenty pounds," said the boy. "I keep that in reserve."

153

The uncle thought it a good joke.

"You keep twenty pounds in reserve, do you, you young romancer? What are you betting, then?"

"I'm betting three hundred," said the boy gravely. "But it's between you and me, Uncle Oscar! Honour bright?"

The uncle burst into a roar of laughter.

"It's between you and me all right, you young Nat Gould," he said, laughing. "But where's your three hundred?"

"Bassett keeps it for me. We're partners."

"You are, are you! And what is Bassett putting on Daffodil?"

"He won't go quite as high as I do, I expect. Perhaps he'll go a hundred and fifty."

"What, pennies?" laughed the uncle.

"Pounds," said the child, with a surprised look at his uncle. "Bassett keeps a bigger reserve than I do."

Between wonder and amusement Uncle Oscar was silent. He pursued the matter no further, but he determined to take his nephew with him to the Lincoln races.

"Now, son," he said, "I'm putting twenty on Mirza, and I'll put five for you on any horse you fancy. What's your pick?"

"Daffodil, uncle."

"No, not the fiver on Daffodil!"

"I should if it was my own fiver," said the child.

"Good! Good! Right you are! A fiver for me and a fiver for you on Daffodil."

The child had never been to a race meeting before, and his eyes were blue fire. He pursed his mouth tight, and watched. A Frenchman just in front had put his money on Lancelot. Wild with excitement, he flayed his arms up and down, yelling "Lancelot! Lancelot!" in his French accent.

Daffodil came in first, Lancelot second, Mirza third. The child, flushed and with eyes blazing, was curiously serene. His uncle brought him four five-pound notes, four to one.

"What am I to do with these?" he cried, waving them before the boy's eyes.

"I suppose we'll talk to Bassett," said the boy. "I expect I have fifteen hundred now; and twenty in reserve; and this twenty."

His uncle studied him for some moments.

"Look here, son!" he said. "You're not serious about Bassett and that fifteen hundred, are you?"

"Yes, I am. But it's between you and me, uncle. Honour bright!"

"Honour bright, all right, son! But I must talk to Bassett."

"If you'd like to be a partner, uncle, with Bassett and me, we could all be partners. Only, you'd have to promise, honour bright, uncle, not to let it go beyond us three. Bassett and I are lucky, and you must be lucky, because it was your ten shillings I started winning with. . . ."

154

Uncle Oscar took both Bassett and Paul into Richmond Park for an afternoon, and there they talked.

"It's like this, you see, sir," Bassett said. "Master Paul would get me talking about racing events, spinning yarns, you know, sir. And he was always keen on knowing if I'd made or if I'd lost. It's about a year since, now, that I put five shillings on Blush of Dawn for him—and we lost. Then the luck turned, with that ten shillings he had from you, that we put on Singhalese. And since that time, it's been pretty steady, all things considering. What do you say, Master Paul?"

"We're all right when we're sure," said Paul. "It's when we're not quite sure that we go down."

"Oh, but we're careful then," said Bassett.

"But when are you sure?" smiled Uncle Oscar.

"It's Master Paul, sir," said Bassett, in a secret, religious voice. "It's as if he had it from heaven. Like Daffodil, now, for the Lincoln. That was as sure as eggs."

"Did you put anything on Daffodil?" asked Oscar Cresswell.

"Yes, sir, I made my bit."

"And my nephew?"

Bassett was obstinately silent, looking at Paul.

"I made twelve hundred, didn't I, Bassett? I told uncle I was putting three hundred on Daffodil."

"That's right," said Bassett, nodding.

"But where's the money?" asked the uncle.

"I keep it safe locked up, sir. Master Paul he can have it any minute he likes to ask for it."

"What, fifteen hundred pounds?"

"And twenty! and forty, that is, with the twenty he made on the course."

"It's amazing!" said the uncle.

"If Master Paul offers you to be partners, sir, I would, if I were you; if you'll excuse me," said Bassett.

Oscar Cresswell thought about it.

"I'll see the money," he said.

They drove home again, and sure enough, Bassett came round to the garden-house with fifteen hundred pounds in notes. The twenty pounds reserve was left with Joe Glee, in the Turf Commission deposit.

"You see, it's all right, uncle, when I'm sure! Then we go strong, for all we're worth. Don't we, Bassett?"

"We do that, Master Paul."

"And when are you sure?" said the uncle, laughing.

"Oh, well, sometimes I'm absolutely sure, like about Daffodil," said the boy; "and sometimes I have an idea; and sometimes I haven't even an idea, have I, Bassett? Then we're careful, because we mostly go down."

"You do, do you! And when you're sure, like about Daffodil, what makes you sure, sonny?"

"Oh, well, I don't know," said the boy uneasily. "I'm sure, you know, uncle; that's all."

"It's as if he had it from heaven, sir," Bassett reiterated.

"I should say so!" said the uncle.

But he became a partner. And when the Leger was coming on, Paul was "sure" about Lively Spark, which was a quite inconsiderable horse. The boy insisted on putting a thousand on the horse, Bassett went for five hundred, and Oscar Cress-well two hundred. Lively Spark came in first, and the betting had been ten to one against him. Paul had made ten thousand.

"You see," he said, "I was absolutely sure of him."

Even Oscar Cresswell had cleared two thousand.

"Look here, son," he said, "this sort of thing makes me nervous."

"It needn't, uncle! Perhaps I shan't be sure again for a long time."

"But what are you going to do with your money?" asked the uncle.

"Of course," said the boy, "I started it for mother. She said she had no luck, because father is unlucky, so I thought if I was lucky, it might stop whispering."

"What might stop whispering?"

"Our house. I hate our house for whispering."

"What does it whisper?"

"Why—why"—the boy fidgeted—"why, I don't know. But it's always short of money, you know, uncle."

"I know it, son, I know it."

"You know people send mother writs, don't you, uncle?"

"I'm afraid I do," said the uncle.

"And then the house whispers, like people laughing at you behind your back. It's awful, that is! I thought if I was lucky..."

"You might stop it," added the uncle.

The boy watched him with big blue eyes that had an uncanny cold fire in them, and he said never a word.

"Well, then!" said the uncle. "What are we doing?"

"I shouldn't like mother to know I was lucky," said the boy.

"Why not, son?"

"She'd stop me."

"I don't think she would."

"Oh!"—and the boy writhed in an odd way—"I don't want her to know, uncle."

"All right, son! We'll manage it without her knowing."

They managed it very easily. Paul, at the other's suggestion, handed over five thousand pounds to his uncle, who deposited it with the family lawyer, who was then to inform Paul's mother that a relative had put five thousand pounds into his hands, which sum was to be paid out a thousand pounds at a time, on the mother's birthday, for the next five years.

156

"So she'll have a birthday present of a thousand pounds for five successive years," said Uncle Oscar. "I hope it won't make it all the harder for her later."

Paul's mother had her birthday in November. The house had been "whispering" worse than ever lately, and, even in spite of his luck, Paul could not bear up against it. He was very anxious to see the effect of the birthday letter, telling his mother about the thousand pounds.

When there were no visitors, Paul now took his meals with his parents, as he was beyond the nursery control. His mother went into town nearly every day. She had discovered that she had an odd knack of sketching furs and dress materials, so she worked secretly in the studio of a friend who was the chief "artist" for the leading drapers. She drew the figures of ladies in furs and ladies in silk and sequins for the newspaper advertisements. This young woman artist earned several thousand pounds a year, but Paul's mother only made several hundreds, and she was again dissatisfied. She so wanted to be first in something, and she did not succeed, even in making sketches for drapery advertisements.

She was down to breakfast on the morning of her birthday. Paul watched her face as she read her letters. He knew the lawyer's letter. As his mother read it, her face hardened and became more expressionless. Then a cold, determined look came on her mouth. She hid the letter under the pile of others, and said not a word about it.

"Didn't you have anything nice in the post for your birthday, mother?" said Paul.

"Quite moderately nice," she said, her voice cold and absent.

She went away to town without saying more.

But in the afternoon Uncle Oscar appeared. He said Paul's mother had had a long interview with the lawyer, asking if the whole five thousand could be advanced at once, as she was in debt.

"What do you think, uncle?" said the boy.

"I leave it to you, son."

"Oh, let her have it, then! We can get some more with the other," said the boy.

"A bird in the hand is worth two in the bush, laddie!" said Uncle Oscar.

"But I'm sure to know for the Grand National; or the Lincolnshire; or else the Derby. I'm sure to know for one of them," said Paul.

So Uncle Oscar signed the agreement, and Paul's mother touched the whole five thousand. Then something very curious happened. The voices in the house suddenly went mad, like a chorus of frogs on a spring evening. There were certain new furnishings, and Paul had a tutor. He was really going to Eton, his father's school, in the following autumn. There were flowers in the winter, and a blossoming of the luxury Paul's mother had been used to. And yet the voices in the house, behind the sprays of mimosa and almond blossom, and from under the piles of iridescent cushions, simply trilled and screamed in a sort of ecstacy: "There must be more money! Oh-h-h, there must be more money. Oh, now, now-w! Now-w-w—there must be more money!—more than ever! More than ever!"

It frightened Paul terribly. He studied away at his Latin and Greek with his tutors. But his intense hours were spent with Bassett. The Grand National had gone by: he had not "known," and had lost a hundred pounds. Summer was at hand. He was in agony for the Lincoln. But even for the Lincoln he didn't "know" and he lost fifty pounds. He became wild-eyed and strange, as if something were going to explode in him.

"Let it alone, son! Don't you bother about it!" urged Uncle Oscar. But it was as if the boy couldn't really hear what his uncle was saying.

"I've got to know for the Derby! I've got to know for the Derby!" the child reiterated, his big blue eyes blazing with a sort of madness.

His mother noticed how overwrought he was.

"You'd better go to the seaside. Wouldn't you like to go now to the seaside, instead of waiting? I think you'd better," she said, looking down at him anxiously, her heart curiously heavy because of him.

But the child lifted his uncanny blue eyes.

"I couldn't possibly go before the Derby, mother!" he said. "I couldn't possibly!"

"Why not?" she said, her voice becoming heavy when she was opposed. "Why not? You can still go from the seaside to see the Derby with your Uncle Oscar, if that's what you wish. No need for you to wait here. Besides, I think you care too much about these races. It's a bad sign. My family has been a gambling family and you won't know till you grow up how much damage it has done. But it has done damage. I shall have to send Bassett away, and ask Uncle Oscar not to talk racing to you, unless you promise to be reasonable about it; go away to the seaside and forget it. You're all nerves!"

"I'll do what you like, mother, so long as you don't send me away till after the Derby," the boy said.

"Send you away from where? Just from this house?"

"Yes," he said, gazing at her.

"Why, you curious child, what makes you care about this house so much, suddenly? I never knew you loved it."

He gazed at her without speaking. He had a secret within a secret, something he had not divulged, even to Bassett or to his Uncle Oscar.

But his mother, after standing undecided and a little bit sullen for some moments, said:

"Very well, then! Don't go to the seaside till after the Derby, if you don't wish it. But promise me you won't let your nerves go to pieces. Promise you won't think so much about horse racing and events, as you call them!"

"Oh, no," said the boy casually. "I won't think much about them, mother. You needn't worry. I wouldn't worry, mother, if I were you."

"If you were me and I were you," said his mother; "I wonder what we should do!"

"But you know you needn't worry, mother, don't you?" the boy repeated.

"I should be awfully glad to know it," she said wearily.

"Oh, well, you can, you know. I mean, you ought to know you needn't worry," he insisted.

"Ought I? Then I'll see about it," she said.

Paul's secret of secrets was his wooden horse, that which had no name. Since he was emancipated from a nurse and a nursery-governess, he had had his rocking horse removed to his own bedroom at the top of the house.

"Surely, you're too big for a rocking horse!" his mother had remonstrated.

"Well, you see, mother, till I can have a real horse, I like to have some sort of animal about," had been his quaint answer.

"Do you feel he keeps you company?" she laughed.

"Oh, yes! He's very good, he always keeps me company, when I'm there," said Paul.

So the horse, rather shabby, stood in an arrested prance in the boy's bedroom.

The Derby was drawing near, and the boy grew more and more tense. He hardly heard what was spoken to him, he was very frail, and his eyes were really uncanny. His mother had sudden seizures of uneasiness about him. Sometimes, for a half-an-hour, she would feel a sudden anxiety about him that was almost anguish. She wanted to rush to him at once, and know he was safe.

Two nights before the Derby, she was at a big party in town, when one of her rushes of anxiety about her boy, her first-born, gripped her heart till she could hardly speak. She fought with the feeling, might and main, for she believed in common sense. But it was too strong. She had to leave the dance and go downstairs to telephone to the country. The children's nursery-governess was terribly surprised and startled at being rung up in the night.

"Are the children all right, Miss Wilmot?"

"Oh, yes, they are quite all right."

"Master Paul? Is he all right?"

"He went to bed as right as a trivet. Shall I run up and look at him?"

"No," said Paul's mother reluctantly. "No! Don't trouble. It's all right. Don't sit up. We shall be home fairly soon." She did not want her son's privacy intruded upon.

"Very good," said the governess.

It was about one o'clock when Paul's mother and father drove up to their

158

house. All was still. Paul's mother went to her room and slipped off her white fur coat. She had told her maid not to wait up for her. She heard her husband downstairs, mixing a whisky-and-soda.

And then, because of the strange anxiety at her heart, she stole upstairs to her son's room. Noiselessly she went along the upper corridor. Was there a faint noise? What was it?

She stood, with arrested muscles, outside his door, listening. There was a strange, heavy, and yet not loud noise. Her heart stood still. It was a soundless noise, yet rushing and powerful. Something huge, in violent, hushed motion. What was it? What in God's name was it? She ought to know. She felt that she knew the noise. She knew what it was.

Yet she could not place it. She couldn't say what it was. And on and on it went, like a madness.

Softly, frozen with anxiety and fear, she turned the door handle.

The room was dark. Yet in the space near the window, she heard and saw something plunging to and fro. She gazed in fear and amazement.

Then suddenly she switched on the light, and saw her son, in his green pyjamas, madly surging on the rocking horse. The blaze of light suddenly lit him up, as he urged the wooden horse, and lit her up, as she stood, blonde, in her dress of pale green and crystal, in the doorway.

"Paul!" she cried. "Whatever are you doing?"

"It's Malabar!" he screamed, in a powerful, strange voice. "It's Malabar."

His eyes blazed at her for one strange and senseless second, as he ceased urging his wooden horse. Then he fell with a crash to the ground, and she, all her tormented motherhood flooding upon her, rushed to gather him up.

But he was unconscious, and unconscious he remained, with some brain-fever. He talked and tossed, and his mother sat stonily by his side.

"Malabar! It's Malabar! Bassett, Bassett, I know! It's Malabar!"

So the child cried, trying to get up and urge the rocking horse that gave him his inspiration.

"What does he mean by Malabar?" asked the heart-frozen mother.

"I don't know," said the father stonily.

"What does he mean by Malabar?" she asked her brother Oscar.

"It's one of the horses running for the Derby," was the answer.

And, in spite of himself, Oscar Cresswell spoke to Bassett, and himself put a thousand on Malabar: at fourteen to one.

The third day of the illness was critical: they were waiting for a change. The boy, with his rather long, curly hair, was tossing ceaselessly on the pillow. He neither slept nor regained consciousness, and his eyes were like blue stones. His mother sat, feeling her heart had gone, turned actually into a stone.

In the evening, Oscar Cresswell did not come, but Bassett sent a message, saying could he come up for one moment, just one moment? Paul's mother was very angry at the intrusion, but on second thought she agreed. The boy was the same. Perhaps Bassett might bring him to consciousness.

The gardener, a shortish fellow with a little brown moustache, and sharp little brown eyes, tiptoed into the room, touched his imaginary cap to Paul's mother, and stole to the bedside, staring with glittering, smallish eyes, at the tossing, dying child.

"Master Paul!" he whispered. "Master Paul! Malabar come in first all right, a clean win. I did as you told me. You've made over seventy thousand pounds, you have; you've got over eighty thousand. Malabar came in all right, Master Paul."

"Malabar! Malabar! Did I say Malabar, mother? Did I say Malabar? Do you think I'm lucky, mother? I knew Malabar, didn't I? Over eighty thousand pounds! I call that lucky, don't you, mother? Over eighty thousand pounds! I knew, didn't I know I knew? Malabar came in all right. If I ride my horse till I'm sure, then I tell you, Bassett, you can go as high as you like. Did you go for all you were worth, Bassett?"

"I went a thousand on it, Master Paul."

"I never told you, mother, that if I can ride my horse, and get there, then I'm absolutely sure—oh, absolutely! Mother, did I ever tell you? I am lucky."

"No, you never did," said the mother.

But the boy died in the night.

And even as he lay dead, his mother heard her brother's voice saying to her: "My God, Hester, you're eighty-odd thousand to the good and a poor devil of a son to the bad. But, poor devil, poor devil, he's best gone out of a life where he rides his rocking horse to find a winner."

EDGAR ALLAN POE   THE BLACK CAT

For the most wild, yet most homely narrative which I am about to pen, I neither
expect nor solicit belief. Mad indeed would I be to expect it, in a case where my
very senses reject their own evidence. Yet, mad am I not—and very surely do I
not dream. But to-morrow I die, and to-day I would unburthen my soul. My
immediate purpose is to place before the world, plainly, succinctly, and
without comment, a series of mere household events. In their consequences,
these events have terrified—have tortured—have destroyed me. Yet I will not
attempt to expound them. To me, they have presented little but Horror—to many
they will seem less terrible than *baroques*. Hereafter, perhaps, some intellect may
be found which will reduce my phantasm to the common-place—some intellect
more calm, more logical, and far less excitable than my own, which will perceive,
in the circumstances I detail with awe, nothing more than an ordinary succession
of very natural causes and effects.

From my infancy I was noted for the docility and humanity of my disposition.
My tenderness of heart was even so conspicuous as to make me the jest of my
companions. I was especially fond of animals, and was indulged by my parents
with a great variety of pets. With these I spent most of my time, and never was so
happy as when feeding and caressing them. This peculiarity of character grew
with my growth, and, in my manhood, I derived from it one of my principal
sources of pleasure. To those who have cherished an affection for a faithful and
sagacious dog, I need hardly be at the trouble of explaining the nature or the intensity of the gratification thus derivable. There is something in the unselfish and
self-sacrificing love of a brute, which goes directly to the heart of him who has
had frequent occasion to test the paltry friendship and gossamer fidelity of mere
Man.

I married early, and was happy to find in my wife a disposition not uncon-
genial with my own. Observing my partiality for domestic pets, she lost no
opportunity of procuring those of the most agreeable kind. We had birds, gold-
fish, a fine dog, rabbits, a small monkey, and *a cat*.

This latter was a remarkably large and beautiful animal, entirely black, and
sagacious to an astonishing degree. In speaking of his intelligence, my wife, who
at heart was not a little tinctured with superstition, made frequent allusion to the
ancient popular notion, which regarded all black cats as witches in disguise. Not

that she was ever *serious* upon this point—and I mention the matter at all for no better reason than that it happens, just now, to be remembered.

Pluto—this was the cat's name—was my favorite pet and playmate. I alone fed him, and he attended me wherever I went about the house. It was even with difficulty that I could prevent him from following me through the streets.

Our friendship lasted, in this manner, for several years, during which my general temperament and character—through the instrumentality of the Fiend Intemperance—had (I blush to confess it) experienced a radical alteration for the worse. I grew, day by day, more moody, more irritable, more regardless of the feelings of others. I suffered myself to use intemperate language to my wife. At length, I even offered her personal violence. My pets, of course, were made to feel the change in my disposition. I not only neglected, but ill-used them. For Pluto, however, I still retained sufficient regard to restrain me from maltreating him, as I made no scruple of maltreating the rabbits, the monkey, or even the dog, when by accident, or through affection, they came in my way. But my disease grew upon me—for what disease is like Alcohol!—and at length even Pluto, who was now becoming old, and consequently somewhat peevish—even Pluto began to experience the effects of my ill temper.

One night, returning home, much intoxicated, from one of my haunts about town, I fancied that the cat avoided my presence. I seized him; when, in his fright at my violence, he inflicted a slight wound upon my hand with his teeth. The fury of a demon instantly possessed me. I knew myself no longer. My original soul seemed, at once, to take its flight from my body; and a more than fiendish malevolence, gin-nurtured, thrilled every fibre of my frame. I took from my waistcoat-pocket a penknife, opened it, grasped the poor beast by the throat, and deliberately cut one of its eyes from the socket! I blush, I burn, I shudder, while I pen the damnable atrocity.

When reason returned with the morning—when I had slept off the fumes of the night's debauch—I experienced a sentiment half of horror, half of remorse, for the crime of which I had been guilty; but it was, at least, a feeble and equivocal feeling, and the soul remained untouched. I again plunged into excess, and soon drowned in wine all memory of the deed.

In the meantime the cat slowly recovered. The socket of the lost eye presented, it is true, a frightful appearance, but he no longer appeared to suffer any pain. He went about the house as usual, but, as might be expected, fled in extreme terror at my approach. I had so much of my old heart left, as to be at first grieved by this evident dislike on the part of a creature which had once so loved me. But this feeling soon gave place to irritation. And then came, as if to my final and irrevocable overthrow, the spirit of PERVERSENESS. Of this spirit philosophy takes no account. Yet I am not more sure that my soul lives, than I am that perverseness is one of the primitive impulses of the human heart—one of the indivisible primary faculties, or sentiments, which give direction to the character of Man. Who has not, a hundred times, found himself committing a vile or a silly action, for no other reason than because he knows he should *not*? Have we not a perpetual in-

162

clination, in the teeth of our best judgment, to violate that which is *Law*, merely because we understand it to be such? This spirit of perverseness, I say, came to my final overthrow. It was this unfathomable longing of the soul *to vex itself*—to offer violence to its own nature—to do wrong for the wrong's sake only—that urged me to continue and finally to consummate the injury I had inflicted upon the unoffending brute. One morning, in cool blood, I slipped a noose about its neck and hung it to the limb of a tree;—hung it with the tears streaming from my eyes, and with the bitterest remorse at my heart;—hung it *because* I knew that it had loved me, and *because* I felt it had given me no reason of offence;—hung it *because* I knew that in so doing I was committing a sin—a deadly sin that would so jeopardize my immortal soul as to place it—if such a thing were possible—even beyond the reach of the infinite mercy of the Most Merciful and Most Terrible God.

163

On the night of the day on which this cruel deed was done, I was aroused from sleep by the cry of fire. The curtains of my bed were in flames. The whole house was blazing. It was with great difficulty that my wife, a servant, and myself, made our escape from the conflagration. The destruction was complete. My entire worldly wealth was swallowed up, and I resigned myself thenceforward to despair.

I am above the weakness of seeking to establish a sequence of cause and effect, between the disaster and the atrocity. But I am detailing a chain of facts—and wish not to leave even a possible link imperfect. On the day succeeding the fire, I visited the ruins. The walls, with one exception, had fallen in. This exception was found in a compartment wall, not very thick, which stood about the middle of the house, and against which had rested the head of my bed. The plastering had here, in great measure, resisted the action of the fire—a fact which I attributed to its having been recently spread. About this wall a dense crowd were collected, and many persons seemed to be examining a particular portion of it with very minute and eager attention. The words "strange!" "singular!" and other similar expressions, excited my curiosity. I approached and saw, as if graven in *bas relief* upon the white surface, the figure of a gigantic *cat*. The impression was given with an accuracy truly marvellous. There was a rope about the animal's neck.

When I first beheld this apparition—for I could scarcely regard it as less—my wonder and my terror were extreme. But at length reflection came to my aid. The cat, I remembered, had been hung in a garden adjacent to the house. Upon the alarm of fire, this garden had been immediately filled by the crowd—by some one of whom the animal must have been cut from the tree and thrown, through an open window, into my chamber. This had probably been done with the view of arousing me from sleep. The falling of other walls had compressed the victim of my cruelty into the substance of the freshly-spread plaster; the lime of which, with the flames, and the *ammonia* from the carcass, had then accomplished the portraiture as I saw it.

Although I thus readily accounted to my reason, if not altogether to my conscience, for the startling fact just detailed, it did not the less fail to make a deep impression upon my fancy. For months I could not rid myself of the phantasm of the cat; and, during this period, there came back into my spirit a half-sentiment that seemed, but was not, remorse. I went so far as to regret the loss of the animal, and to look about me, among the vile haunts which I now habitually frequented, for another pet of the same species, and of somewhat similar appearance, with which to supply its place.

One night as I sat, half stupefied, in a den of more than infamy, my attention was suddenly drawn to some black object, reposing upon the head of one of the immense hogsheads of Gin, or of Rum, which constituted the chief furniture of the apartment. I had been looking steadily at the top of this hogshead for some minutes, and what now caused me surprise was the fact that I had not sooner perceived the object thereupon. I approached it, and touched it with my hand. It was a black cat—a very large one—fully as large as Pluto, and closely resembling him in every respect but one. Pluto had not a white hair upon any portion of his body; but this cat had a large, although indefinite splotch of white, covering nearly the whole region of the breast.

Upon my touching him, he immediately arose, purred loudly, rubbed against my hand, and appeared delighted with my notice. This, then, was the very creature of which I was in search. I at once offered to purchase it of the landlord; but this person made no claim to it—knew nothing of it—had never seen it before.

I continued my caresses, and, when I prepared to go home, the animal evinced a disposition to accompany me. I permitted it to do so; occasionally stooping and patting it as I proceeded. When it reached the house it domesticated itself at once, and became immediately a great favorite with my wife.

For my own part, I soon found a dislike to it arising within me. This was just the reverse of what I had anticipated; but I know not how or why it was—its evident fondness for myself rather disgusted and annoyed. By slow degrees, these feelings of disgust and annoyance rose into the bitterness of hatred. I avoided the creature; a certain sense of shame, and the remembrance of my former deed of cruelty, preventing me from physically abusing it. I did not, for some weeks, strike, or otherwise violently ill use it; but gradually—very gradually—I came to look upon it with unutterable loathing, and to flee silently from its odious presence, as from the breath of a pestilence.

What added, no doubt, to my hatred of the beast, was the discovery, on the morning after I brought it home, that, like Pluto, it also had been deprived of one of its eyes. This circumstance, however, only endeared it to my wife, who, as I have already said, possessed, in a high degree, that humanity of feeling which had once been my distinguishing trait, and the source of many of my simplest and purest pleasures.

With my aversion to this cat, however, its partiality for myself seemed to increase. It followed my footsteps with a pertinacity which it would be difficult to make the reader comprehend. Whenever I sat, it would crouch beneath my chair, or spring upon my knees, covering me with its loathsome caresses. If I arose to walk it would get between my feet and thus nearly throw me down, or, fastening its long and sharp claws in my dress, clamber, in this manner, to my breast. At such times, although I longed to destroy it with a blow, I was yet withheld from so doing, partly by a memory of my former crime, but chiefly—let me confess it at once—by absolute *dread* of the beast.

This dread was not exactly a dread of physical evil—and yet I should be at a loss how otherwise to define it. I am almost ashamed to own—yes, even in this felon's cell, I am almost ashamed to own—that the terror and horror with which the animal inspired me, had been heightened by one of the merest chimæras it would be possible to conceive. My wife had called my attention, more than once, to the character of the mark of white hair, of which I have spoken, and which constituted the sole visible difference between the strange beast and the one I had destroyed. The reader will remember that this mark, although large, had been originally very indefinite; but, by slow degrees—degrees nearly imperceptible, and which for a long time my Reason struggled to reject as fanciful—it had, at length, assumed a rigorous distinctness of outline. It was now the representation of an object that I shudder to name—and for this, above all, I loathed, and dreaded, and would have rid myself of the monster *had I dared*—it was now, I say, the image of a hideous—of a ghastly thing—of the GALLOWS!—oh, mournful and terrible engine of Horror and of Crime—of Agony and of Death!

And now was I indeed wretched beyond the wretchedness of mere Humanity. And a *brute beast*—whose fellow I had contemptuously destroyed—*a brute beast* to work out for *me*—for me a man, fashioned in the image of the High God—so much of insufferable wo! Alas! neither by day nor by night knew I the blessing of Rest any more! During the former the creature left me no moment alone; and, in the latter, I started, hourly, from dreams of unutterable fear, to find the hot breath of *the thing* upon my face, and its vast weight—an incarnate Night-Mare that I had no power to shake off—incumbent eternally upon my *heart!*

Beneath the pressure of torments such as these, the feeble remnant of the good within me succumbed. Evil thoughts became my sole intimates—the darkest and most evil of thoughts. The moodiness of my usual temper increased to hatred of all things and of all mankind; while, from the sudden, frequent, and ungovernable outbursts of a fury to which I now blindly abandoned myself, my uncomplaining wife, alas! was the most usual and the most patient of sufferers.

One day she accompanied me, upon some household errand, into the cellar of the old building which our poverty compelled us to inhabit. The cat followed me down the steep stairs, and, nearly throwing me headlong, exasperated me to madness. Uplifting an axe, and forgetting, in my wrath, the childish dread which had hitherto stayed my hand, I aimed a blow at the animal which, of course, would have proved instantly fatal had it descended as I wished. But this blow was arrested by the hand of my wife. Goaded, by the interference, into a rage more than demoniacal, I withdrew my arm from her grasp and buried the axe in her brain. She fell dead upon the spot, without a groan.

This hideous murder accomplished, I set myself forthwith, and with entire deliberation, to the task of concealing the body. I knew that I could not remove it from the house, either by day or by night, without the risk of being observed by the neighbors. Many projects entered my mind. At one period I thought of cutting the corpse into minute fragments, and destroying them by fire. At another, I resolved to dig a grave for it in the floor of the cellar. Again, I deliberated about casting it in the well in the yard—about packing it in a box, as if merchandize, with the usual arrangements, and so getting a porter to take it from the house. Finally I hit upon what I considered a far better expedient than either of these. I determined to wall it up in the cellar—as the monks of the middle ages are recorded to have walled up their victims.

For a purpose such as this the cellar was well adapted. Its walls were loosely constructed and had lately been plastered throughout with a rough plaster, which the dampness of the atmosphere had prevented from hardening. Moreover, in one of the walls was a projection, caused by a false chimney, or fireplace, that had been filled up, and made to resemble the rest of the cellar. I made no doubt that I could readily displace the bricks at this point, insert the corpse, and wall the whole up as before, so that no eye could detect anything suspicious.

And in this calculation I was not deceived. By means of a crow-bar I easily dislodged the bricks, and, having carefully deposited the body against the inner wall, I propped it in that position, while, with little trouble, I re-laid the whole structure as it originally stood. Having procured mortar, sand, and hair, with every possible precaution, I prepared a plaster which could not be distinguished from the old, and with this I very carefully went over the new brick-work. When I had finished, I felt satisfied that all was right. The wall did not present the slightest appearance of having been disturbed. The rubbish on the floor was picked up with the minutest care. I looked around triumphantly, and said to myself—"Here at least, then, my labor has not been in vain."

My next step was to look for the beast which had been the cause of so much wretchedness; for I had, at length, firmly resolved to put it to death. Had I been able to meet with it, at the moment, there could have been no doubt of its fate, but it appeared that the crafty animal had been alarmed at the violence of my previous anger, and forebore to present itself in my present mood. It is impossible to describe, or to imagine, the deep, the blissful sense of relief which the absence of the detested creature occasioned in my bosom. It did not make its appearance during the night—and thus for one night at least, since its introduction into the house, I soundly and tranquilly slept; aye, *slept* even with the burden of murder upon my soul!

The second and the third day passed, and still my tormentor came not. Once again I breathed as a freeman. The monster, in terror, had fled the premises forever! I should behold it no more! My happiness was supreme! The guilt of my dark deed disturbed me but little. Some few inquiries had been made, but these had been readily answered. Even a search had been instituted—but of course nothing was to be discovered. I looked upon my future felicity as secured.

Upon the fourth day of the assassination, a party of police came, very un-expectedly, into the house, and proceeded again to make rigorous investigation of the premises. Secure, however, in the inscrutability of my place of conceal-ment, I felt no embarassment whatever. The officers bade me accompany them in their search. They left no nook or corner unexplored. At length, for the third or fourth time, they descended into the cellar. I quivered not in a muscle. My heart beat calmly as that of one who slumbers in innocence. I walked the cellar from end to end. I folded my arms upon my bosom, and roamed easily to and fro. The police were thoroughly satisfied and prepared to depart. The glee at my heart was too strong to be restrained. I burned to say if but one word, by way of triumph, and to render doubly sure their assurance of my guiltlessness.

"Gentlemen," I said at last, as the party ascended the steps, "I delight to have allayed your suspicions. I wish you all health, and a little more courtesy. By the bye, gentlemen, this—this is a very well-constructed house." [In the rabid desire to say something easily, I scarcely knew what I uttered at all.]—"I may say an *excellently* well-constructed house. These walls—are you going, gentlemen?—these walls are solidly put together;" and here, through the mere phrenzy of bravado, I rapped heavily, with a cane which I held in my hand, upon that very portion of the brick-work behind which stood the corpse of the wife of my bosom.

But may God shield and deliver me from the fangs of the Arch-Fiend! No sooner had the reverberation of my blows sunk into silence, than I was answered by a voice from within the tomb!—by a cry, at first muffled and broken, like the sobbing of a child, and then quickly swelling into one long, loud, and continuous scream, utterly anomalous and inhuman—a howl!—a wailing shriek, half of horror and half of triumph, such as might have arisen only out of hell, conjointly from the throats of the damned in their agony and of the demons that exult in the damnation.

Of my own thoughts it is folly to speak. Swooning, I staggered to the opposite wall. For one instant the party upon the stairs remained motionless, through extremity of terror and of awe. In the next, a dozen stout arms were toiling at the wall. It fell bodily. The corpse, already greatly decayed and clotted with gore, stood erect before the eyes of the spectators. Upon its head, with red extended mouth and solitary eye of fire, sat the hideous beast whose craft had seduced me into murder, and whose informing voice had consigned me to the hangman. I had walled the monster up within the tomb!

167

168   They were new patients to me, all I had was the name, Olson. Please come down as soon as you can, my daughter is very sick.

When I arrived I was met by the mother, a big startled-looking woman, very clean and apologetic who merely said, Is this the doctor? and let me in. In the back, she added. You must excuse us, doctor, we have her in the kitchen where it is warm. It is very damp here sometimes.

The child was fully dressed and sitting on her father's lap near the kitchen table. He tried to get up, but I motioned for him not to bother, took off my overcoat and started to look things over. I could see that they were all very nervous, eyeing me up and down distrustfully. As often, in such cases, they weren't telling me more than they had to, it was up to me to tell them; that's why they were spending three dollars on me.

The child was fairly eating me up with her cold, steady eyes, and no expression to her face whatever. She did not move and seemed, inwardly, quiet; an unusually attractive little thing, and as strong as a heifer in appearance. But her face was flushed, she was breathing rapidly, and I realized that she had a high fever. She had magnificent blonde hair, in profusion. One of those picture children often reproduced in advertising leaflets and the photogravure sections of the Sunday papers.

She's had a fever for three days, began the father and we don't know what it comes from. My wife has given her things, you know, like people do, but it don't do no good. And there's been a lot of sickness around. So we tho't you'd better look her over and tell us what is the matter.

As doctors often do I took a trial shot at it as a point of departure. Has she had a sore throat?

Both parents answered me together, No ... No, she says her throat don't hurt her.

Does your throat hurt you? added the mother to the child. But the little girl's expression didn't change nor did she move her eyes from my face.

Have you looked?

I tried to, said the mother, but I couldn't see.

As it happens we had been having a number of cases of diphtheria in the school to which this child went during that month and we were all, quite apparently, thinking of that, though no one had as yet spoken of the thing.

Well, I said, suppose we take a look at the throat first. I smiled in my best professional manner and asking for the child's first name I said, come on, Mathilda, open you mouth and let's take a look at your throat.

Nothing doing.

Aw, come on, I coaxed, just open your mouth wide and let me take a look. Look, I said opening both hands wide, I haven't anything in my hands. Just open up and let me see.

Such a nice man, put in the mother. Look how kind he is to you. Come on, do what he tells you to. He won't hurt you.

At that I ground my teeth in disgust. If only they wouldn't use the word "hurt" I might be able to get somewhere. But I did not allow myself to be hurried or disturbed but speaking quietly and slowly I approached the child again.

As I moved my chair a little nearer suddenly with one cat-like movement both her hands clawed instinctively for my eyes and she almost reached them too. In fact she knocked my glasses flying and they fell, though unbroken, several feet away from me on the kitchen floor.

Both the mother and father almost turned themselves inside out in embarrassment and apology. You bad girl, said the mother, taking her and shaking her by one arm. Look what you've done. The nice man . . .

For heaven's sake, I broke in. Don't call me a nice man to her. I'm here to look at her throat on the chance that she might have diphtheria and possibly die of it. But that's nothing to her. Look here, I said to the child, we're going to look at your throat. You're old enough to understand what I'm saying. Will you open it now by yourself or shall we have to open it for you?

Not a move. Even her expression hadn't changed. Her breaths however were coming faster and faster. Then the battle began. I had to do it. I had to have a throat culture for her own protection. But first I told the parents that it was entirely up to them. I explained the danger but said that I would not insist on a throat examination so long as they would take the responsibility.

If you don't do what the doctor says you'll have to go to the hospital, the mother admonished her severely.

Oh yeah? I had to smile to myself. After all, I had already fallen in love with the savage brat, the parents were contemptible to me. In the ensuing struggle they grew more and more abject, crushed, exhausted while she surely rose to magnificent heights of insane fury of effort bred of her terror of me.

The father tried his best, and he was a big man but the fact that she was his daughter, his shame at her behavior and his dread of hurting her made him release her just at the critical times when I had almost achieved success, till I wanted to kill him. But his dread also that she might have diphtheria made him

169

tell me to go on, go on though he himself was almost fainting, while the mother moved back and forth behind us raising and lowering her hands in an agony of apprehension.

Put her in front of you on your lap, I ordered, and hold both her wrists.

But as soon as he did the child let out a scream. Don't, you're hurting me. Let go of my hands. Let them go I tell you. Then she shrieked terrifyingly, hysterically. Stop it! Stop it! You're killing me!

Do you think she can stand it, doctor! said the mother.

You get out, said the husband to his wife. Do you want her to die of diphtheria?

Come on now, hold her, I said.

Then I grasped the child's head with my left hand and tried to get the wooden tongue depressor between her teeth. She fought, with clenched teeth, desperately! But now I also had grown furious—at a child. I tried to hold myself down but I couldn't. I know how to expose a throat for inspection. And I did my best. When finally I got the wooden spatula behind the last teeth and just the point of it into the mouth cavity, she opened up for an instant but before I could see anything she came down again and gripping the wooden blade between her molars she reduced it to splinters before I could get it out again.

Aren't you ashamed, the mother yelled at her. Aren't you ashamed to act like that in front of the doctor?

Get me a smooth-handled spoon of some sort, I told the mother. We're going through with this. The child's mouth was already bleeding. Her tongue was cut and she was screaming in wild hysterical shrieks. Perhaps I should have desisted and come back in an hour or more. No doubt it would have been better. But I have seen at least two children lying dead in bed of neglect in such cases, and feeling that I must get a diagnosis now or never I went at it again. But the worst of it was that I too had got beyond reason. I could have torn the child apart in my own fury and enjoyed it. It was a pleasure to attack her. My face was burning with it.

The damned little brat must be protected against her own idiocy, one says to one's self at such times. Others must be protected against her. It is a social necessity. And all these things are true. But a blind fury, a feeling of adult shame, bred of a longing for muscular release are the operatives. One goes on to the end.

In a final unreasoning assault I overpowered the child's neck and jaws. I forced the heavy silver spoon back of her teeth and down her throat till she gagged. And there it was—both tonsils covered with membrane. She had fought valiantly to keep me from knowing her secret. She had been hiding that sore throat for three days at least and lying to her parents in order to escape just such an outcome as this.

Now truly she was furious. She had been on the defensive before but now she attacked. Tried to get off her father's lap and fly at me while tears of defeat blinded her eyes.

AMBROSE BIERCE   THE BOARDED WINDOW

In 1830, only a few miles away from what is now the great city of Cincinnati, lay an immense and almost unbroken forest. The whole region was sparsely settled by people of the frontier—restless souls who no sooner had hewn fairly habitable homes out of the wilderness and attained to that degree of prosperity which today we should call indigence than impelled by some mysterious impulse of their nature they abandoned all and pushed farther westward, to encounter new perils and privations in the effort to regain the meagre comforts which they had voluntarily renounced. Many of them had already forsaken that region for the remoter settlements, but among those remaining was one who had been of those first arriving. He lived alone in a house of logs surrounded on all sides by the great forest, of whose gloom and silence he seemed a part, for no one had ever known him to smile nor speak a needless word. His simple wants were supplied by the sale or barter of skins of wild animals in the river town, for not a thing did he grow upon the land which, if needful, he might have claimed by right of undisturbed possession. There were evidences of "improvement"—a few acres of ground immediately about the house had once been cleared of its trees, the decayed stumps of which were half concealed by the new growth that had been suffered to repair the ravage wrought by the ax. Apparently the man's zeal for agriculture had burned with a failing flame, expiring in penitential ashes.

The little log house, with its chimney of sticks, its roof of warping clapboards weighted with traversing poles and its "chinking" of clay, had a single door and, directly opposite, a window. The latter, however, was boarded up—nobody could remember a time when it was not. And none knew why it was so closed; certainly not because of the occupant's dislike of light and air, for on those rare occasions when a hunter had passed that lonely spot the recluse had commonly been seen sunning himself on his doorstep if heaven had provided sunshine for his need. I fancy there are few persons living today who ever knew the secret of that window, but I am one, as you shall see.

The man's name was said to be Murlock. He was apparently seventy years old, actually about fifty. Something besides years had had a hand in his aging. His hair and long, full beard were white, his gray, lustreless eyes sunken, his face singularly seamed with wrinkles which appeared to belong to two intersecting systems. In figure he was tall and spare, with a stoop of the shoulders—a burden bearer. I never saw him; these particulars I learned from my grandfather, from whom also I got the man's story when I was a lad. He had known him when living near by in that early day.

One day Murlock was found in his cabin, dead. It was not a time and place for coroners and newspapers, and I suppose it was agreed that he had died from natural causes or I should have been told, and should remember. I know only that with what was probably a sense of the fitness of things the body was buried near the cabin, alongside the grave of his wife, who had preceded him by so many years that local tradition had retained hardly a hint of her existence. That closes the final chapter of this true story—excepting, indeed, the circumstances that many years afterward, in company with an equally intrepid spirit, I penetrated to the place and ventured near enough to the ruined cabin to throw a stone against it, and ran away to avoid the ghost which every well-informed boy thereabout knew haunted the spot. But there is an earlier chapter—that supplied by my grandfather.

When Murlock built his cabin and began laying sturdily about with his ax to hew out a farm—the rifle, meanwhile, his means of support—he was young, strong, and full of hope. In that eastern country whence he came he had married, as was the fashion, a young woman in all ways worthy of his honest devotion, who shared the dangers and privations of his lot with a willing spirit and light heart. There is no known record of her name; of her charms of mind and person tradition is silent and the doubter is at liberty to entertain his doubt; but God forbid that I should share it! Of their affection and happiness there is abundant assurance in every added day of the man's widowed life; for what but the magnetism of a blessed memory could have chained that venturesome spirit to a lot like that?

One day Murlock returned from gunning in a distant part of the forest to find his wife prostrate with fever, and delirious. There was no physician within miles, no neighbor; nor was she in a condition to be left, to summon help. So he set about the task of nursing her back to health, but at the end of the third day she fell into unconsciousness and so passed away, apparently, with never a gleam of returning reason.

From what we know of a nature like his we may venture to sketch in some of the details of the outline picture drawn by my grandfather. When convinced that she was dead, Murlock had sense enough to remember that the dead must be prepared for burial. In performance of this sacred duty he blundered now and again, did certain things incorrectly, and others which he did correctly were done over and over. His occasional failures to accomplish some simple and ordinary act filled him with astonishment, like that of a drunken man who wonders at the suspension of familiar natural laws. He was surprised, too, that he did not weep—surprised and a little ashamed; surely it is unkind not to weep for the dead. "Tomorrow," he said aloud, "I shall have to make the coffin and dig the grave; and then I shall miss her, when she is no longer in sight; but now—she is dead, of course, but it is all right—it *must* be all right, somehow. Things cannot be so bad as they seem."

172

He stood over the body in the fading light, adjusting the hair and putting the finishing touches to the simple toilet, doing all mechanically, with soulless care. And still through his consciousness ran an undersense of conviction that all was right—that he should have her again as before, and everything explained. He had had no experience in grief; his capacity had not been enlarged by use. His heart could not contain it all, nor his imagination rightly conceive it. He did not know he was so hard struck; *that* knowledge would come later, and never go. Grief is an artist of powers as various as the instruments upon which he plays his dirges for the dead, evoking from some the sharpest, shrillest notes, from others the low, grave chords that throb recurrent like the slow beating of a distant drum. Some natures it startles; some it stupefies. To one it comes like the stroke of an arrow, stinging all the sensibilities to a keener life; to another as the blow of a bludgeon, which in crushing benumbs. We may conceive Murlock to have been that way affected, for (and here we are upon surer ground than that of conjecture) no sooner had he finished his pious work than, sinking into a chair by the side of the table upon which the body lay, and noting how white the profile showed in the deepening gloom, he laid his arms upon the table's edge, and dropped his face into them, tearless yet and unutterably weary. At that moment came in through the open window a long, wailing sound like the cry of a lost child in the far deeps of the darkening wood! But the man did not move. Again, and nearer than before, sounded that unearthly cry upon his failing sense. Perhaps it was a wild beast; perhaps it was a dream. For Murlock was asleep.

Some hours later, as it afterward appeared, this unfaithful watcher awoke and lifting his head from his arms intently listened—he knew not why. There in the black darkness by the side of the dead, recalling all without a shock, he strained his eyes to see—he knew not what. His senses were alert, his breath was suspended, his blood had stilled its tides as if to assist the silence. Who—what had waked him, and where was it?

Suddenly the table shook beneath his arms, and at the same moment he heard, or fancied that he heard, a light, soft step—another—sounds as of bare feet upon the floor!

He was terrified beyond the power to cry out or move. Perforce he waited—waited there in the darkness through seeming centuries of such dread as one may know, yet live to tell. He tried vainly to speak the dead woman's name, vainly to stretch forth his hand across the table to learn if she were there. His throat was powerless, his arms and hands were like lead. Then occurred something most frightful. Some heavy body seemed hurled against the table with an impetus that pushed it against his breast so sharply as nearly to overthrow him, and at the same instant he heard and felt the fall of something upon the floor with so violent a thump that the whole house was shaken by the impact. A scuffling ensued, and a confusion of sounds impossible to describe. Murlock had risen to his feet. Fear had by excess forfeited control of his faculties. He flung his hands upon the table. Nothing was there!

There is a point at which terror may turn to madness; and madness incites to action. With no definite intent, from no motive but the wayward impulse of

173

a madman, Murlock sprang to the wall, with a little groping seized his loaded rifle, and without aim discharged it. By the flash which lit up the room with a vivid illumination, he saw an enormous panther dragging the dead woman toward the window, its teeth fixed in her throat! Then there were darkness blacker than before, and silence; and when he returned to consciousness the sun was high and the wood vocal with songs of birds.

The body lay near the window, where the beast had left it when frightened away by the flash and report of the rifle. The clothing was deranged, the long hair in disorder, the limbs lay anyhow. From the throat, dreadfully lacerated, had issued a pool of blood not yet entirely coagulated. The ribbon with which he had bound the wrists was broken; the hands were tightly clenched. Between the teeth was a fragment of the animal's ear.

174

J. F. POWERS   THE VALIANT WOMAN

They had come to the dessert in a dinner that was a shambles. "Well, John," **175**
Father Nulty said, turning away from Mrs. Stoner and to Father Firman, long
gone silent at his own table. "You've got the bishop coming for confirmations
next week."

"Yes," Mrs. Stoner cut in, "and for dinner. And if he don't eat any more than
he did last year—"

Father Firman, in a rare moment, faced it. "Mrs. Stoner, the bishop is not
well. You know that."

"And after I fixed that fine dinner and all." Mrs. Stoner pouted in Father
Nulty's direction.

"I wouldn't feel bad about it, Mrs. Stoner," Father Nulty said. "He never eats
much anywhere."

"It's funny. And that new Mrs. Allers said he ate just fine when he was
there," Mrs. Stoner argued, and then spit out, "but she's a damned liar!"

Father Nulty, unsettled but trying not to show it, said, "Who's Mrs. Allers?"

"She's at Holy Cross," Mrs. Stoner said.

"She's the housekeeper," Father Firman added, thinking Mrs. Stoner made it
sound as though Mrs. Allers were the pastor there.

"I swear I don't know what to do about the dinner this year," Mrs. Stoner said.

Father Firman moaned. "Just do as you've always done, Mrs. Stoner."

"Huh! And have it all to throw out! Is that any way to do?"

"Is there any dessert?" Father Firman asked coldly.

Mrs. Stoner leaped up from the table and bolted into the kitchen, mumbling.
She came back with a birthday cake. She plunged it in the center of the table.
She found a big wooden match in her apron pocket and thrust it at Father Firman.

"I don't like this bishop," she said. "I never did. And the way he went and
cut poor Ellen Kennedy out of Father Doolin's will!"

She went back into the kitchen.

"Didn't they talk a lot of filth about Doolin and the housekeeper?" Father
Nulty asked.

"I should think they did," Father Firman said. "All because he took her to the movies on Sunday night. After he died and the bishop cut her out of the will, though I hear he gives her a pension privately, they talked about the bishop."

"I don't like this bishop at all," Mrs. Stoner said, appearing with a cake knife. "Bishop Doran—there was the man!"

"We know," Father Firman said. "All man and all priest."

"He did know real estate," Father Nulty said.

Father Firman struck the match.

"Not on the chair!" Mrs. Stoner cried, too late.

Father Firman set the candle burning—it was suspiciously large and yellow, like a blessed one, but he could not be sure. They watched the fluttering flame.

"I'm forgetting the lights!" Mrs. Stoner said, and got up to turn them off. She went into the kitchen again.

The priests had a moment of silence in the candlelight.

"Happy birthday, John," Father Nulty said softly. "Is it fifty-nine you are?"

"As if you didn't know, Frank," Father Firman said, "and you the same but one."

Father Nulty smiled, the old gold of his incisors shining in the flickering light, his collar whiter in the dark, and raised his glass of water, which would have been wine or better in the bygone days, and toasted Father Firman.

"Many of 'em, John."

"Blow it out," Mrs. Stoner said, returning to the room. She waited by the light switch for Father Firman to blow out the candle.

Mrs. Stoner, who ate no desserts, began to clear the dishes into the kitchen, and the priests, finishing their cake and coffee in a hurry, went to sit in the study.

Father Nulty offered a cigar.

"John?"

"My ulcers, Frank."

"Ah, well, you're better off." Father Nulty lit the cigar and crossed his long black legs. "Fish Frawley has got him a Filipino, John. Did you hear?"

Father Firman leaned forward, interested. "He got rid of the woman he had?"

"He did. It seems she snooped."

"Snooped, eh?"

"She did. And gossiped. Fish introduced two town boys to her, said, 'Would you think these boys were my nephews?' That's all, and the next week the paper had it that his two nephews were visiting him from Erie. After that, he let her believe he was going East to see his parents, though both are dead. The paper carried the story. Fish returned and made a sermon out of it. Then he got the Filipino."

Father Firman squirmed with pleasure in his chair. "That's like Fish, Frank. He can do that." He stared at the tips of his fingers bleakly. "You could never get a Filipino to come to a place like this."

"Probably not," Father Nulty said. "Fish is pretty close to Minneapolis. Ah, say, do you remember the trick he played on us all in Marmion Hall!"

"That I'll not forget!" Father Firman's eyes remembered. "Getting up New Year's morning and finding the toilet seats all painted!"

"*Happy Circumcision!* Hah!" Father Nulty had a coughing fit.

When he had got himself together again, a mosquito came and sat on his wrist. He watched it a moment before bringing his heavy hand down. He raised his hand slowly, viewed the dead mosquito, and sent it spinning with a plunk of his middle finger.

"Only the female bites," he said.

"I didn't know that," Father Firman said.

"Ah, yes . . ."

Mrs. Stoner entered the study and sat down with some sewing—Father Firman's black socks.

She smiled pleasantly at Father Nulty. "And what do you think of the atom bomb, Father?"

"Not much," Father Nulty said.

Mrs. Stoner had stopped smiling. Father Firman yawned.

Mrs. Stoner served up another: "Did you read about this communist convert, Father?"

"He's been in the Church before," Father Nulty said, "and so it's not a conversion, Mrs. Stoner."

"No? Well, I already got him down on my list of Monsignor's converts."

"It's better than a conversion, Mrs. Stoner, for there is more rejoicing in heaven over the return of . . . uh, he that was lost, Mrs. Stoner, is found."

"And that congresswoman, Father?"

"Yes. A convert—she."

"And Henry Ford's grandson, Father. I got him down."

"Yes, to be sure."

Father Firman yawned, this time audibly, and held his jaw.

"But he's one only by marriage, Father," Mrs. Stoner said. "I always say you got to watch those kind."

"Indeed you do, but a convert nonetheless, Mrs. Stoner. Remember, Cardinal Newman himself was one."

Mrs. Stoner was unimpressed. "I see where Henry Ford's making steering wheels out of soybeans, Father."

"I didn't see that."

"I read it in the *Reader's Digest* or some place."

"Yes, well . . ." Father Nulty rose and held his hand out to Father Firman. "John," he said. "It's been good."

"I heard Hirohito's next," Mrs. Stoner said, returning to converts.

"Let's wait and see, Mrs. Stoner," Father Nulty said.

The priests walked to the door.

"You know where I live, John."

"Yes. Come again Frank. Good night."

Father Firman watched Father Nulty go down the walk to his car at the curb. He hooked the screen door and turned off the porch light. He hesitated at the foot of the stairs, suddenly moved to go to bed. But he went back into his study.

"Phew!" Mrs. Stoner said. "I thought he'd never go. Here it is after eight o'clock."

Father Firman sat down in his rocking chair. "I don't see him often," he said.

"I give up!" Mrs. Stoner exclaimed, flinging the holey socks upon the horsehair sofa. "I'd swear you had a nail in your shoe."

"I told you I looked."

"Well, you ought to look again. And cut your toenails, why don't you? Haven't I got enough to do?"

178   Father Firman scratched in his coat pocket for a pill, found one, swallowed it. He let his head sink back against the chair and closed his eyes. He could hear her moving about the room, making the preparations; and how he knew them— the fumbling in the drawer for a pencil with a point, the rip of the page from his daily calendar, and finally the leg of the card table sliding up against his leg.

He opened his eyes. She yanked the floor lamp alongside the table, setting the bead fringe tinkling on the shade, and pulled up her chair on the other side. She sat down and smiled at him for the first time that day. Now she was happy.

She swept up the cards and began to shuffle with the abandoned virtuosity of an old river-boat gambler, standing them on end, fanning them out, whirling them through her fingers, dancing them halfway up her arms, cracking the whip over them. At last they lay before him tamed into a neat deck.

"Cut?"

"Go ahead," he said. She liked to go first.

She gave him her faint, avenging smile and drew a card, cast it aside for another which he thought must be an ace from the way she clutched it face down.

She was getting all the cards, as usual, and would have been invincible if she had possessed his restraint and if her cunning had been of a higher order. He knew a few things about leading and lying back that she would never learn. Her strategy was attack, forever attack, with one baffling departure: she might sacrifice certain tricks as expendable if only she could have the last ones, the heartbreaking ones, if she could slap them down one after another, shatteringly.

She played for blood, no bones about it, but for her there was no other way; it was her nature, as it was the lion's, and for this reason he found her ferocity pardonable, more a defect of the flesh, venial, while his own trouble was all in the will, mortal. He did not sweat and pray over each card as she must, but he did keep an eye out for reneging and demanded a cut now and then just to aggravate her, and he was always secretly hoping for aces.

With one card left in her hand, the telltale trick coming next, she delayed playing it, showing him first the smile, the preview of defeat. She laid it on the table— so! She held one more trump than he had reasoned possible. Had she palmed it from somewhere? No, she would not go that far; that would not be fair, was worse than reneging, which so easily and often happened accidentally, and she believed in being fair. Besides he had been watching her.

God smote the vines with hail, the sycamore trees with frost, and offered up the flocks to the lightning—but Mrs. Stoner! What a cross Father Firman had from God in Mrs. Stoner! There were other housekeepers as bad, no doubt, walking the rectories of the world, yes, but . . . yes. He could name one and maybe two priests who were worse off. One, maybe two. Cronin. His scraggly blonde of sixty—take her, with her everlasting banging on the grand piano, the gift of the pastor; her proud talk about the goiter operation at the Mayo Brothers', also a gift; her honking the parish Buick at passing strange priests because they were all in the game together. She was worse. She was something to keep the home fires burning. Yes sir. And Cronin said she was not a bad person really, but what was he? He was quite a freak himself.

For that matter, could anyone say that Mrs. Stoner was a bad person? No. He could not say it himself, and he was no freak. She had her points, Mrs. Stoner. She was clean. And though she cooked poorly, could not play the organ, would not take up the collection in an emergency, and went to card parties, and told all— even so, she was clean. She washed everything. Sometimes her underwear hung down beneath her dress like a paratrooper's pants, but it and everything she touched was clean. She washed constantly. She was clean.

She had her other points, to be sure—her faults, you might say. She snooped— no mistake about it—but it was not snooping for snooping's sake; she had a reason. She did other things, always with a reason. She overcharged on rosaries and prayer books, but that was for the sake of the poor. She censored the pamphlet rack, but that was to prevent scandal. She pried into the baptismal and matrimonial records, but there was no other way if Father was out, and in this way she had uncovered a bastard and flushed him out of the rectory, but that was the perverted decency of the times. She held her nose over bad marriages in the presence of the victims, but that was her sorrow and came from having her husband buried in a mine. And he had caught her telling a bewildered young couple that there was only one good reason for their wanting to enter into a mixed marriage—the child had to have a name, and that—that was what?

She hid his books, kept him from smoking, picked his friends (usually the pastors of her colleagues), bawled out people for calling after dark, had no humor, except at cards, and then it was grim, very grim, and sat hatchet-faced every morning at Mass. But she went to Mass, which was all that kept the church from being empty some mornings. She did annoying things all day long. She said annoying things into the night. She said she had given him the best years of her life. Had she? Perhaps—for the miner had her only a year. It was too bad, sinfully bad, when he thought of it like that. But all talk of best years and life was nonsense. He had to consider the heart of the matter, the essence. The essence was that housekeepers were hard to get, harder to get than ushers, than willing workers, than organists, than secretaries—yes, harder to get than assistants or vocations.

And she was a *saver*—saved money, saved electricity, saved string, bags, sugar, saved—him. That's what she did. That's what she said she did, and she was right, in a way. In a way, she was usually right. In fact, she was always right—in a way. And you could never get a Filipino to come way out here and live. Not a young one

179

anyway, and he had never seen an old one. Not a Filipino. They liked to dress up and live.

Should he let it drop about Fish having one, just to throw a scare into her, let her know he was doing some thinking? No. It would be a perfect cue for the one about a man needing a woman to look after him. He was not up to that again, not tonight.

Now she was doing what she liked most of all. She was making a grand slam, playing it out card for card, though it was in the bag, prolonging what would have been cut short out of mercy in gentle company. Father Firman knew the agony of losing.

She slashed down the last card, a miserable deuce trump, and did in the hapless king of hearts he had been saving.

"Skunked you!"

She was awful in victory. Here was the bitter end of their long day together, the final murderous hour in which all they wanted to say—all he wouldn't and all she couldn't—came out in the cards. Whoever won at honeymoon won the day, slept on the other's scalp, and God alone had to help the loser.

"We've been at it long enough, Mrs. Stoner," he said, seeing her assembling the cards for another round.

"Had enough, huh!"

Father Firman grumbled something.

"No?"

"Yes."

She pulled the table away and left it against the wall for the next time. She went out of the study carrying the socks, content and clucking. He closed his eyes after her and began to get under way in the rocking chair, the nightly trip to nowhere. He could hear her brewing a cup of tea in the kitchen and conversing with the cat. She made her way up the stairs, carrying the tea, followed by the cat purring.

He waited, rocking out to sea, until she would be sure to be through in the bathroom. Then he got up and locked the front door (she looked after the back door) and loosened his collar going upstairs.

In the bathroom he mixed a glass of antiseptic, always afraid of pyorrhea, and gargled to ward off pharyngitis.

When he turned on the light in his room, the moths and beetles began to batter against the screens, the lighter insects humming. . . .

Yes, and she had the guest room. How did she come to get that? Why wasn't she in the back room, in her proper place? He knew, if he cared to remember. The screen in the back room—it let in mosquitoes, and if it didn't do that she'd love to sleep back there, Father, looking out at the steeple and the blessed cross on top, Father, if it just weren't for the screen, Father. Very well, Mrs. Stoner, I'll get it fixed or fix it myself. Oh, could you now, Father? I could, Mrs. Stoner, and I will. In the meantime you take the guest room. Yes, Father, and thank you, Father, the house ringing with amenities then. Years ago, all that. She was a pie-faced girl then, not really a girl perhaps, but not too old to marry again. But she never had. In fact, he could not remember that she had even tried for a husband since coming to the rectory, but, of course, he could be wrong, not knowing how they went about it. God! God save us! Had she got her wires crossed and mistaken him all these years for *that? That!* Him! Suffering God! No. That was going too far. That was getting morbid. No. He must not think of that again, ever. No.

But just the same she had got the guest room and she had it yet. Well, did it matter? Nobody ever came to see him any more, nobody to stay overnight anyway, nobody to stay very long . . . not any more. He knew how they laughed at him. He had heard Frank humming all right—before he saw how serious and sad the situation was and took pity—humming, "Wedding Bells Are Breaking Up That Old Gang of Mine." But then they'd always laughed at him for something—for not being an athlete, for wearing glasses, for having kidney trouble . . . and mail coming addressed to Rev. and Mrs. Stoner.

181

Removing his shirt, he bent over the table to read the volume left open from last night. He read, translating easily, 'Eisdem licet cum illis . . . Clerics are allowed to reside only with women about whom there can be no suspicion, either because of a natural bond (as mother, sister, aunt) or of advanced age, combined in both cases with good repute."

Last night he had read it, and many nights before, each time as though this time to find what was missing, to find what obviously was not in the paragraph, his problem considered, a way out. She was neither mother, sister, nor aunt, and *advanced age* was a relative term (why, she was younger than he was) and so, eureka, she did not meet the letter of the law—but, alas, how she fulfilled the spirit! And besides it would be a slimy way of handling it after all her years of service. He could not afford to pension her off, either.

He slammed the book shut. He slapped himself fiercely on the back, missing the wily mosquito, and whirled to find it. He took a magazine and folded it into a swatter. Then he saw it—oh, the preternatural cunning of it!—poised in the beard of St. Joseph on the bookcase. He could not hit it there. He teased it away, wanting it to light on the wall, but it knew his thoughts and flew high away. He swung wildly, hoping to stun it, missed, swung back, catching St. Joseph across the neck. The statue fell to the floor and broke.

Mrs. Stoner was panting in the hall outside his door.

"What is it!"

"Mosquitoes!"

"What is it, Father? Are you hurt?"

"Mosquitoes—damn it! And only the female bites!"

Mrs. Stoner, after a moment, said, "Shame on you, Father. She needs the blood for her eggs."

He dropped the magazine and lunged at the mosquito with his bare hand.

She went back to her room, saying, "Pshaw, I thought it was burglars murdering you in your bed."

He lunged again.

182   All the trouble began when my grandfather died and my grandmother—my father's mother—came to live with us. Relations in the one house are a strain at the best of times, but, to make matters worse, my grandmother was a real old countrywoman and quite unsuited to the life in town. She had a fat, wrinkled old face, and, to Mother's great indignation, went round the house in bare feet— the boots had her crippled, she said. For dinner she had a jug of porter and a pot of potatoes with—sometimes—a bit of salt fish, and she poured out the potatoes on the table and ate them slowly, with great relish, using her fingers by way of a fork.

  Now, girls are supposed to be fastidious, but I was the one who suffered most from this. Nora, my sister, just sucked up to the old woman for the penny she got every Friday out of the old-age pension, a thing I could not do. I was too honest, that was my trouble; and when I was playing with Bill Connell, the sergeant-major's son, and saw my grandmother steering up the path with the jug of porter sticking out from beneath her shawl I was mortified. I made excuses not to let him come into the house, because I could never be sure what she would be up to when we went in.

  When Mother was at work and my grandmother made the dinner I wouldn't touch it. Nora once tried to make me, but I hid under the table from her and took the bread-knife with me for protection. Nora let on to be very indignant (she wasn't, of course, but she knew Mother saw through her, so she sided with Gran) and came after me. I lashed out at her with the bread-knife, and after that she left me alone. I stayed there till Mother came in from work and made my dinner, but when Father came in later Nora said in a shocked voice: "Oh, Dadda, do you know what Jackie did at dinnertime?" Then, of course, it all came out; Father gave me a flaking; Mother interfered, and for days after that he didn't speak to me and Mother barely spoke to Nora. And all because of that old woman! God knows, I was heart-scalded.

Then, to crown my misfortunes, I had to make my first confession and communion. It was an old woman called Ryan who prepared us for these. She was
about the one age with Gran; she was well-to-do, lived in a big house on
Montenotte, wore a black cloak and bonnet, and came every day to school at
three o'clock when we should have been going home, and talked to us of hell.
She may have mentioned the other place as well, but that could only have been
by accident, for hell had the first place in her heart.

She lit a candle, took out a new half-crown, and offered it to the first boy who
would hold one finger—only one finger!—in the flame for five minutes by the
school clock. Being always very ambitious I was tempted to volunteer, but I
thought it might look greedy. Then she asked were we afraid of holding one
finger—only one finger!—in a little candle flame for five minutes and not afraid
of burning all over in roasting hot furnaces for all eternity. "All eternity! Just
think of that! A whole lifetime goes by and it's nothing, not even a drop in the
ocean of your sufferings." The woman was really interesting about hell, but my
attention was all fixed on the half-crown. At the end of the lesson she put it back
in her purse. It was a great disappointment; a religious woman like that, you
wouldn't think she'd bother about a thing like a half-crown.

Another day she said she knew a priest who woke one night to find a fellow
he didn't recognize leaning over the end of his bed. The priest was a bit frightened
—naturally enough—but he asked the fellow what he wanted, and the fellow
said in a deep, husky voice that he wanted to go to confession. The priest said
it was an awkward time and wouldn't it do in the morning, but the fellow said that
last time he went to confession, there was one sin he kept back, being ashamed
to mention it, and now it was always on his mind. Then the priest knew it was
a bad case, because the fellow was after making a bad confession and committing
a mortal sin. He got up to dress, and just then the cock crew in the yard outside,
and—lo and behold!—when the priest looked around there was no sign of the
fellow, only a smell of burning timber, and when the priest looked at his bed
didn't he see the print of two hands burned in it? That was because the fellow
had made a bad confession. This story made a shocking impression on me.

But the worst of all was when she showed us how to examine our conscience.
Did we take the name of the Lord, our God, in vain? Did we honour our father
and our mother? (I asked her did this include grandmothers and she said it did.)
Did we love our neighbours as ourselves? Did we covet our neighbour's goods?
(I thought of the way I felt about the penny that Nora got every Friday.) I decided
that, between one thing and another, I must have broken the whole ten command-
ments, all on account of that old woman, and so far as I could see, so long as she
remained in the house I had no hope of ever doing anything else.

I was scared to death of confession. The day the whole class went I let on to
have a toothache, hoping my absence wouldn't be noticed; but at three o'clock,
just as I was feeling safe, along comes a chap with a message from Mrs. Ryan
that I was to go to confession myself on Saturday and be at the chapel for communion with the rest. To make it worse, Mother couldn't come with me and sent
Nora instead.

Now, that girl had ways of tormenting me that Mother never knew of. She held my hand as we went down the hill, smiling sadly and saying how sorry she was for me, as if she were bringing me to the hospital for an operation.

"Oh, God help us!" she moaned. "Isn't it a terrible pity you weren't a good boy? Oh, Jackie, my heart bleeds for you! How will you ever think of all your sins? Don't forget you have to tell him about the time you kicked Gran on the shin."

"Lemme go!" I said, trying to drag myself free of her. "I don't want to go to confession at all."

"But sure, you'll have to go to confession, Jackie," she replied in the same regretful tone. "Sure, if you didn't, the parish priest would be up to the house, looking for you. 'Tisn't, God knows, that I'm not sorry for you. Do you remember the time you tried to kill me with the bread-knife under the table? And the language you used to me? I don't know what he'll do with you at all, Jackie. He might have to send you up to the bishop."

I remember thinking bitterly that she didn't know the half of what I had to tell— if I told it. I knew I couldn't tell it, and understood perfectly why the fellow in Mrs. Ryan's story made a bad confession; it seemed to me a great shame that people wouldn't stop criticizing him. I remember that steep hill down to the church, and the sunlit hillsides beyond the valley of the river, which I saw in the gaps between the houses like Adam's last glimpse of Paradise.

Then, when she had manœuvred me down the long flight of steps to the chapel yard, Nora suddenly changed her tone. She became the raging malicious devil she really was.

"There you are!" she said with a yelp of triumph, hurling me through the church door. "And I hope he'll give you the penitential psalms, you dirty little caffler."

I knew then I was lost, given up to eternal justice. The door with the coloured-glass panels swung shut behind me, the sunlight went out and gave place to deep shadow, and the wind whistled outside so that the silence within seemed to crackle like ice under my feet. Nora sat in front of me by the confession box. There were a couple of old women ahead of her, and then a miserable-looking poor devil came and wedged me in at the other side, so that I couldn't escape even if I had the courage. He joined his hands and rolled his eyes in the direction of the roof, muttering aspirations in an anguished tone, and I wondered had he a grandmother too. Only a grandmother could account for a fellow behaving in that heartbroken way, but he was better off than I, for he at least could go and confess his sins; while I would make a bad confession and then die in the night and be continually coming back and burning people's furniture.

Nora's turn came, and I heard the sound of something slamming, and then her voice as if butter wouldn't melt in her mouth, and then another slam, and out she came. God, the hypocrisy of women! Her eyes were lowered, her head was bowed, and her hands were joined very low down on her stomach, and she walked up the aisle to the side altar looking like a saint. You never saw such an exhibition of devotion; and I remembered the devilish malice with which she had tormented me all the way from our door, and wondered were all religious people like that, really. It was my turn now. With the fear of damnation in my soul I went in, and the confessional door closed of itself behind me.

It was pitch-dark and I couldn't see priest or anything else. Then I really began to be frightened. In the darkness it was a matter between God and me, and He had all the odds. He knew what my intentions were before I even started; I had no chance. All I had ever been told about confession got mixed up in my mind, and I knelt to one wall and said: "Bless me, father, for I have sinned; this is my first confession." I waited for a few minutes, but nothing happened, so I tried it on the other wall. Nothing happened there either. He had me spotted all right.

It must have been then that I noticed the shelf at about one height with my head. It was really a place for grown-up people to rest their elbows, but in my distracted state I thought it was probably the place you were supposed to kneel. Of course, it was on the high side and not very deep, but I was always good at climbing and managed to get up all right. Staying up was the trouble. There was room only for my knees, and nothing you could get a grip on but a sort of wooden moulding a bit above it. I held on to the moulding and repeated the words a little louder, and this time something happened all right. A slide was slammed back; a little light entered the box, and a man's voice said: "Who's there?"

185

"'Tis me, father," I said for fear he mightn't see me and go away again. I couldn't see him at all. The place the voice came from was under the moulding, about level with my knees, so I took a good grip on the moulding and swung myself down till I saw the astonished face of a young priest looking up at me. He had to put his head on one side to see me, and I had to put mine on one side to see him, so we were more or less talking to one another upsidedown. It struck me as a queer way of hearing confessions, but I didn't feel it my place to criticize.

"Bless me, father, for I have sinned; this is my first confession," I rattled off in all one breath, and swung myself down the last shade more to make it easier for him.

"What are you doing up there?" he shouted in an angry voice, and the strain the politeness was putting on my hold of the moulding, and the shock of being addressed in such an uncivil tone, were too much for me. I lost my grip, tumbled, and hit the door an unmerciful wallop before I found myself flat on my back in the middle of the aisle. The people who had been waiting stood up with their mouths open. The priest opened the door of the middle box and came out, pushing his biretta back from his forehead; he looked something terrible. Then Nora came scampering down the aisle.

"Oh, you dirty little caffler!" she said. "I might have known you'd do it. I might have known you'd disgrace me. I can't leave you out of my sight for one minute."

Before I could even get to my feet to defend myself she bent down and gave me a clip across the ear. This reminded me that I was so stunned I had even forgotten to cry, so that people might think I wasn't hurt at all, when in fact I was probably maimed for life. I gave a roar out of me.

"What's all this about?" the priest hissed, getting angrier than ever and pushing Nora off me. "How dare you hit the child like that, you little vixen?"

"But I can't do my penance with him, father," Nora cried, cocking an outraged eye up at him.

"Well, go and do it, or I'll give you some more to do," he said, giving me a hand up. "Was it coming to confession you were, my poor man?" he asked me.

"'Twas, father," said I with a sob.

"Oh," he said respectfully, "a big hefty fellow like you must have terrible sins. Is this your first?"

"'Tis, father," said I.

"Worse and worse," he said gloomily. "The crimes of a lifetime. I don't know will I get rid of you at all today. You'd better wait now till I'm finished with these old ones. You can see by the looks of them they haven't much to tell."

"I will, father," I said with something approaching joy.

The relief of it was really enormous. Nora stuck out her tongue at me from behind his back, but I couldn't even be bothered retorting. I knew from the very moment that man opened his mouth that he was intelligent above the ordinary. When I had time to think, I saw how right I was. It only stood to reason that a fellow confessing after seven years would have more to tell than people that went every week. The crimes of a lifetime, exactly as he said. It was only what he expected, and the rest was the cackle of old women and girls with their talk of hell, the bishop, and the penitential psalms. That was all they knew. I started to make my examination of conscience, and barring the one bad business of my grandmother it didn't seem so bad.

The next time, the priest steered me into the confession box himself and left the shutter back the way I could see him get in and sit down at the further side of the grille from me.

"Well, now," he said, "what do they call you?"

"Jackie, father," said I.

"And what's a-trouble to you, Jackie?"

"Father," I said, feeling I might as well get it over while I had him in good humour, "I had it all arranged to kill my grandmother."

He seemed a bit shaken by that, all right, because he said nothing for quite a while.

"My goodness," he said at last, "that'd be a shocking thing to do. What put that into your head?"

"Father," I said, feeling very sorry for myself, "she's an awful woman."

"Is she?" he asked. "What way is she awful?"

"She takes porter, father," I said, knowing well from the way Mother talked of it that this was a mortal sin, and hoping it would make the priest take a more favourable view of my case.

"Oh, my!" he said, and I could see he was impressed.

"And snuff, father," said I.

"That's a bad case, sure enough, Jackie," he said.

"And she goes round in her bare feet, father," I went on in a rush of self-pity, "and she knows I don't like her, and she gives pennies to Nora and none to me, and my da sides with her and flakes me, and one night I was so heart-scalded I made up my mind I'd have to kill her."

"And what would you do with the body?" he asked with great interest.

"I was thinking I could chop that up and carry it away in a barrow I have," I said.

"Begor, Jackie," he said, "do you know you're a terrible child?"

"I know, father," I said, for I was just thinking the same thing myself. "I tried to kill Nora too with a bread-knife under the table, only I missed her."

"Is that the little girl that was beating you just now?" he asked.

"'Tis, father."

"Someone will go for her with a bread-knife one day, and he won't miss her," he said rather cryptically. "You must have great courage. Between ourselves, there's a lot of people I'd like to do the same to but I'd never have the nerve. Hanging is an awful death."

187

"Is it, father?" I asked with the deeper interest—I was always very keen on hanging. "Did you ever see a fellow hanged?"

"Dozens of them," he said solemnly. "And they all died roaring."

"Jay!" I said.

"Oh, a horrible death!" he said with great satisfaction. "Lots of the fellows I saw killed their grandmothers too, but they all said 'twas never worth it."

He had me there for a full ten minutes talking, and then walked out the chapel yard with me. I was genuinely sorry to part with him, because he was the most entertaining character I'd ever met in the religious line. Outside, after the shadow of the church, the sunlight was like the roaring of waves on a beach; it dazzled me; and when the frozen silence melted and I heard the screech of trams on the road my heart soared. I knew now I wouldn't die in the night and come back, leaving marks on my mother's furniture. It would be a great worry to her, and the poor soul had enough.

Nora was sitting on the railing, waiting for me, and she put on a very sour puss when she saw the priest with me. She was mad jealous because a priest had never come out of the church with her.

"Well," she asked coldly, after he left me, "what did he give you?"

"Three Hail Marys," I said.

"Three Hail Marys," she repeated incredulously. "You mustn't have told him anything."

"I told him everything," I said confidently.

"About Gran and all?"

"About Gran and all."

(All she wanted was to be able to go home and say I'd made a bad confession.)

"Did you tell him you went for me with the bread-knife?" she asked with a frown.

"I did to be sure."

"And he only gave you three Hail Marys?"

"That's all."

She slowly got down from the railing with a baffled air. Clearly, this was beyond her. As we mounted the steps back to the main road she looked at me suspiciously.

"What are you sucking?" she asked.

"Bullseyes."

"Was it the priest gave them to you?"

"'Twas."

"Lord God," she wailed bitterly, "some people have all the luck! 'Tis no advantage to anybody trying to be good. I might just as well be a sinner like you."

WILLIAM FAULKNER   A ROSE FOR EMILY

1

When Miss Emily Grierson died, our whole town went to her funeral: the men through a sort of respectful affection for a fallen monument, the women mostly out of curiosity to see the inside of her house, which no one save an old man-servant—a combined gardener and cook—had seen in at least ten years.

It was a big, squarish frame house that had once been white, decorated with cupolas and spires and scrolled balconies in the heavily lightsome style of the seventies, set on what had once been our most select street. But garages and cotton gins had encroached and obliterated even the august names of that neighborhood; only Miss Emily's house was left, lifting its stubborn and coquettish decay above the cotton wagons and the gasoline pumps—an eyesore among eyesores. And now Miss Emily had gone to join the representatives of those august names where they lay in the cedar-bemused cemetery among the ranked and anonymous graves of Union and Confederate soldiers who fell at the battle of Jefferson.

Alive, Miss Emily had been a tradition, a duty, and a care: a sort of hereditary obligation upon the town, dating from that day in 1894 when Colonel Sartoris, the mayor—he who fathered the edict that no Negro woman should appear on the streets without an apron—remitted her taxes, the dispensation dating from the death of her father on into perpetuity. Not that Miss Emily would have accepted charity. Colonel Sartoris invented an involved tale to the effect that Miss Emily's father had loaned money to the town, which the town, as a matter of business, preferred this way of repaying. Only a man of Colonel Sartoris' generation and thought could have invented it, and only a woman could have believed it.

When the next generation, with its more modern ideas, became mayors and aldermen, this arrangement created some little dissatisfaction. On the first of the year they mailed her a tax notice. February came, and there was no reply. They wrote her a formal letter, asking her to call at the sheriff's office at her convenience. A week later the mayor wrote her himself, offering to call or to send his car for her, and received in reply a note on paper of an archaic shape, in a thin, flowing calligraphy in faded ink, to the effect that she no longer went out at all. The tax notice was also enclosed, without comment.

They called a special meeting of the Board of Aldermen. A deputation waited upon her, knocked at the door through which no visitor had passed since she ceased giving china-painting lessons eight or ten years earlier. They were admitted by the old Negro into a dim hall from which a stairway mounted into still more shadow. It smelled of dust and disuse—a close, dank smell. The Negro led them into the parlor. It was furnished in heavy, leather-covered furniture. When the Negro opened the blinds of one window, they could see that the leather was cracked; and when they sat down, a faint dust rose sluggishly about their thighs, spinning with slow motes in the single sunray. On a tarnished gilt easel before the fireplace stood a crayon portrait of Miss Emily's father.

They rose when she entered—a small, fat woman in black, with a thin gold chain descending to her waist and vanishing into her belt, leaning on an ebony cane with a tarnished gold head. Her skeleton was small and spare; perhaps that was why what would have been merely plumpness in another was obesity in her. She looked bloated, like a body long submerged in motionless water, and of that pallid hue. Her eyes, lost in the fatty ridges of her face, looked like two small pieces of coal pressed into a lump of dough as they moved from one face to another while the visitors stated their errand.

She did not ask them to sit. She just stood in the door and listened quietly until the spokesman came to a stumbling halt. Then they could hear the invisible watch ticking at the end of the gold chain.

Her voice was dry and cold. "I have no taxes in Jefferson. Colonel Sartoris explained it to me. Perhaps one of you can gain access to the city records and satisfy yourselves."

"But we have. We are the city authorities, Miss Emily. Didn't you get a notice from the sheriff, signed by him?"

"I received a paper, yes," Miss Emily said. "Perhaps he considers himself the sheriff . . . I have no taxes in Jefferson."

"But there is nothing on the books to show that, you see. We must go by the—"

"See Colonel Sartoris. I have no taxes in Jefferson."

"But, Miss Emily—"

"See Colonel Sartoris." (Colonel Sartoris had been dead almost ten years.) "I have no taxes in Jefferson. Tobe!" The Negro appeared. "Show these gentlemen out."

2

So she vanquished them, horse and foot, just as she had vanquished their fathers thirty years before about the smell. That was two years after her father's death and a short time after her sweetheart—the one we believed would marry her—had deserted her. After her father's death she went out very little; after her sweetheart went away, people hardly saw her at all. A few of the ladies had the temerity to call, but were not received, and the only sign of life about the place was the Negro man—a young man then— going in and out with a market basket.

"Just as if a man—any man—could keep a kitchen properly," the ladies said; so they were not surprised when the smell developed. It was another link between the gross, teeming world and the high and mighty Griersons.

A neighbor, a woman, complained to the mayor, Judge Stevens, eighty years old. "But what will you have me do about it, madam?" he said.

"Why, send her word to stop it," the woman said. "Isn't there a law?"

"I'm sure that won't be necessary," Judge Stevens said. "It's probably just a snake or a rat that nigger of hers killed in the yard. I'll speak to him about it."

The next day he received two more complaints, one from a man who came in diffident deprecation. "We really must do something about it, Judge. I'd be the last one in the world to bother Miss Emily, but we've got to do something." That night the Board of Aldermen met—three graybeards and one younger man, a member of the rising generation.

"It's simple enough," he said. "Send her word to have her place cleaned up. Give her a certain time to do it in, and if she don't . . ."

"Dammit, sir," Judge Stevens said, "will you accuse a lady to her face of smelling bad?"

So the next night, after midnight, four men crossed Miss Emily's lawn and slunk about the house like burglars, sniffing along the base of the brickwork and at the cellar openings while one of them performed a regular sowing motion with his hand out of a sack slung from his shoulder. They broke open the cellar door and sprinkled lime there, and in all the out-buildings. As they recrossed the lawn, a window that had been dark was lighted and Miss Emily sat in it, the light behind her, and her upright torso motionless as that of an idol. They crept quietly across the lawn and into the shadow of the locusts that lined the street. After a week or two the smell went away.

That was when people had begun to feel really sorry for her. People in our town, remembering how old lady Wyatt, her great-aunt, had gone completely crazy at last, believed that the Griersons held themselves a little too high for what they really were. None of the young men were quite good enough for Miss Emily and such. We had long thought of them as a tableau, Miss Emily a slender figure in white in the background, her father a spraddled silhouette in the foreground, his back to her and clutching a horsewhip, the two of them framed by the back-flung front door. So when she got to be thirty and was still single, we were not pleased exactly, but vindicated; even with insanity in the family she wouldn't have turned down all of her chances if they had really materialized.

When her father died, it got about that the house was all that was left to her; and in a way, people were glad. At last they could pity Miss Emily. Being left alone, and a pauper, she had become humanized. Now she too would know the old thrill and the old despair of a penny more or less.

The day after his death all the ladies prepared to call at the house and offer condolence and aid, as is our custom. Miss Emily met them at the door, dressed as usual and with no trace of grief on her face. She told them that her father was not dead. She did that for three days, with the ministers calling on her, and the doctors, trying to persuade her to let them dispose of the body. Just as they were about to resort to law and force, she broke down, and they buried her father quickly.

We did not say she was crazy then. We believed she had to do that. We remembered all the young men her father had driven away, and we knew that with nothing left, she would have to cling to that which had robbed her, as people will.

3

She was sick for a long time. When we saw her again, her hair was cut short, making her look like a girl, with a vague resemblance to those angels in colored church windows—sort of tragic and serene.

The town had just let the contracts for paving the sidewalks, and in the summer after her father's death they began the work. The construction company came with niggers and mules and machinery, and a foreman named Homer Barron, a Yankee—a big, dark, ready man, with a big voice and eyes lighter than his face. The little boys would follow in groups to hear him cuss the niggers, and the niggers singing in time to the rise and fall of picks. Pretty soon he knew everybody in town. Whenever you heard a lot of laughing anywhere about the square, Homer Barron would be in the center of the group. Presently we began to see him and Miss Emily on Sunday afternoons driving in the yellow-wheeled buggy and the matched team of bays from the livery stable.

At first we were glad that Miss Emily would have an interest, because the ladies all said, "Of course a Grierson would not think seriously of a Northerner, a day laborer." But there were still others, older people, who said that even grief could not cause a real lady to forget noblesse oblige—without calling it noblesse oblige. They just said, "Poor Emily. Her kinsfolk should come to her." She had some kin in Alabama; but years ago her father had fallen out with them over the estate of old lady Wyatt, the crazy woman, and there was no communication between the two families. They had not even been represented at the funeral.

And as soon as the old people said, "Poor Emily," the whispering began. "Do you suppose it's really so?" they said to one another. "Of course it is. What else could . . ." This behind their hands; rustling of craned silk and satin behind jalousies closed upon the sun of Sunday afternoon as the thin, swift clop-clop-clop of the matched team passed: "Poor Emily."

She carried her head high enough—even when we believed that she was fallen. It was as if she demanded more than ever the recognition of her dignity as the last Grierson; as if it had wanted that touch of earthiness to reaffirm her imperviousness. Like when she bought the rat poison, the arsenic. That was over a year after they had begun to say "Poor Emily," and while the two female cousins were visiting her.

"I want some poison," she said to the druggist. She was over thirty then, still a slight woman, though thinner than usual, with cold, haughty black eyes in a face the flesh of which was strained across the temples and about the eyesockets as you imagine a lighthouse-keeper's face ought to look. "I want some poison," she said.

"Yes, Miss Emily. What kind? For rats and such? I'd recom—"

"I want the best you have. I don't care what kind."

The druggist named several. "They'll kill anything up to an elephant. But what you want is—"

"Arsenic," Miss Emily said. "Is that a good one?"

"Is . . . arsenic? Yes, ma'am. But what you want—"

"I want arsenic."

The druggist looked down at her. She looked back at him, erect, her face like a strained flag. "Why, of course," the druggist said. "If that's what you want. But the law requires you to tell what you are going to use it for."

Miss Emily just stared at him, her head tilted back in order to look him eye for eye, until he looked away and went and got the arsenic and wrapped it up. The Negro delivery boy brought her the package; the druggist didn't come back. When she opened the package at home there was written on the box, under the skull and bones: "For rats."

4

So the next day we all said, "She will kill herself"; and we said it would be the best thing. When she had first begun to be seen with Homer Barron, we had said, "She will marry him." Then we said, "She will persuade him yet," because Homer himself had remarked—he liked men, and it was known that he drank with the younger men in the Elks' Club—that he was not a marrying man. Later we said, "Poor Emily" behind the jalousies as they passed on Sunday afternoon in the glittering buggy, Miss Emily with her head high and Homer Barron with his hat cocked and a cigar in his teeth, reins and whip in a yellow glove.

Then some of the ladies began to say that it was a disgrace to the town and a bad example to the young people. The men did not want to interfere, but at last the ladies forced the Baptist minister—Miss Emily's people were Episcopal—to call upon her. He would never divulge what happened during that interview, but he refused to go back again. The next Sunday they again drove about the streets, and the following day the minister's wife wrote to Miss Emily's relations in Alabama.

So she had blood-kin under her roof again and we sat back to watch developments. At first nothing happened. Then we were sure that they were to be married. We learned that Miss Emily had been to the jeweler's and ordered a man's toilet set in silver, with the letters H. B. on each piece. Two days later we learned that she had bought a complete outfit of men's clothing, including a nightshirt, and we said, "They are married." We were really glad. We were glad because the two female cousins were even more Grierson than Miss Emily had ever been.

So we were not surprised when Homer Barron—the streets had been finished some time since—was gone. We were a little disappointed that there was not a public blowing-off, but we believed that he had gone on to prepare for Miss Emily's coming, or to give her a chance to get rid of the cousins. (By that time it was a cabal, and we were all Miss Emily's allies to help circumvent the cousins.) Sure enough, after another week they departed. And, as we had expected all along, within three days Homer Barron was back in town. A neighbor saw the Negro man admit him at the kitchen door at dusk one evening.

And that was the last we saw of Homer Barron. And of Miss Emily for some time. The Negro man went in and out with the market basket, but the front door remained closed. Now and then we would see her at a window for a moment, as the men did that night when they sprinkled the lime, but for almost six months she did not appear on the streets. Then we knew that this was to be expected too; as if that quality of her father which had thwarted her woman's life so many times had been too virulent and too furious to die.

When we next saw Miss Emily, she had grown fat and her hair was turning gray. During the next few years it grew grayer and grayer until it attained an even pepper-and-salt iron-gray, when it ceased turning. Up to the day of her death at seventy-four it was still that vigorous iron-gray, like the hair of an active man.

From that time on her front door remained closed, save during a period of six or seven years, when she was about forty, during which she gave lessons in china-painting. She fitted up a studio in one of the downstairs rooms, where the daughters and granddaughters of Colonel Sartoris' contemporaries were sent to her with the same regularity and in the same spirit that they were sent to church on Sundays with a twenty-five-cent piece for the collection plate. Meanwhile her taxes had been remitted.

Then the newer generation became the backbone and the spirit of the town, and the painting pupils grew up and fell away and did not send their children to her with boxes of color and tedious brushes and pictures cut from the ladies' magazines. The front door closed upon the last one and remained closed for good. When the town got free postal delivery, Miss Emily alone refused to let them fasten the metal numbers above her door and attach a mailbox to it. She would not listen to them.

Daily, monthly, yearly we watched the Negro grow grayer and more stooped, going in and out with the market basket. Each December we sent her a tax notice, which would be returned by the post office a week later, unclaimed. Now and then we would see her in one of the downstairs windows—she had evidently shut up the top floor of the house—like the carven torso of an idol in a niche, looking or not looking at us, we could never tell which. Thus she passed from generation to generation—dear, inescapable, impervious, tranquil, and perverse.

And so she died. Fell ill in the house filled with dust and shadows, with only a doddering Negro man to wait on her. We did not even know she was sick; we had long since given up trying to get any information from the Negro. He talked to no one, probably not even to her, for his voice had grown harsh and rusty, as if from disuse.

She died in one of the downstairs rooms, in a heavy walnut bed with a curtain, her gray head propped on a pillow yellow and moldy with age and lack of sunlight.

5

The Negro met the first of the ladies at the front door and let them in, with their hushed, sibilant voices and their quick, curious glances, and then he disappeared. He walked right through the house and out the back and was not seen again.

The two female cousins came at once. They held the funeral on the second day, with the town coming to look at Miss Emily beneath a mass of bought flowers, with the crayon face of her father musing profoundly above the bier and the ladies sibilant and macabre; and the very old men—some in their brushed Confederate uniforms—on the porch and the lawn, talking of Miss Emily as if she had been a contemporary of theirs, believing that they had danced with her and courted her perhaps, confusing time with its mathematical progression, as the old do, to whom all the past is not a diminishing road but, instead, a huge meadow which no winter ever quite touches, divided from them now by the narrow bottle-neck of the most recent decade of years.

Already we knew that there was one room in that region above stairs which no one had seen in forty years, and which would have to be forced. They waited until Miss Emily was decently in the ground before they opened it.

The violence of breaking down the door seemed to fill this room with pervading dust. A thin, acrid pall as of the tomb seemed to lie everywhere upon this room decked and furnished as for a bridal: upon the valance curtains of faded rose color, upon the rose-shaded lights, upon the dressing table, upon the delicate array of crystal and the man's toilet things backed with tarnished silver, silver so tarnished that the monogram was obscured. Among them lay a collar and tie, as if they had just been removed, which, lifted, left upon the surface a pale crescent in the dust. Upon a chair hung the suit, carefully folded; beneath it the two mute shoes and the discarded socks.

The man himself lay in the bed.

For a long while we just stood there, looking down at the profound and fleshless grin. The body had apparently once lain in the attitude of an embrace, but now the long sleep that outlasts love, that conquers even the grimace of love, had cuckolded him. What was left of him, rotted beneath what was left of the nightshirt, had become inextricable from the bed in which he lay; and upon him and upon the pillow beside him lay that even coating of the patient and biding dust.

Then we noticed that in the second pillow was the indentation of a head. One of us lifted something from it, and leaning forward, that faint and invisible dust dry and acrid in the nostrils, we saw a long strand of iron-gray hair.

196   The grandmother didn't want to go to Florida. She wanted to visit some of her connections in east Tennessee and she was seizing at every chance to change Bailey's mind. Bailey was the son she lived with, her only boy. He was sitting on the edge of his chair at the table, bent over the orange sports section of the *Journal*. "Now look here, Bailey," she said, "see here, read this," and she stood with one hand on her thin hip and the other rattling the newspaper at his bald head. "Here this fellow that calls himself The Misfit is aloose from the Federal Pen and headed toward Florida and you read what it says he did to these people. Just you read it. I wouldn't take my children in any direction with a criminal like that aloose in it. I couldn't answer to my conscience if I did."

Bailey didn't look up from his reading so she wheeled around then and faced the children's mother, a young woman in slacks, whose face was as broad and innocent as a cabbage and was tied around with a green headkerchief that had two points on the top like rabbit's ears. She was sitting on the sofa, feeding the baby his apricots out of a jar. "The children have been to Florida before," the old lady said. "You all ought to take them somewhere else for a change so they would see different parts of the world and be broad. They never have been to east Tennessee."

The children's mother didn't seem to hear her but the eight-year-old boy, John Wesley, a stocky child with glasses, said, "If you don't want to go to Florida, why dontcha stay at home?" He and the little girl, June Star, were reading the funny papers on the floor.

"She wouldn't stay at home to be queen for a day," June Star said without raising her yellow head.

"Yes, and what would you do if this fellow, The Misfit, caught you?" the grandmother asked.

"I'd smack his face," John Wesley said.

"She wouldn't stay at home for a million bucks," June Star said. "Afraid she'd miss something. She has to go everywhere we go."

"All right, Miss," the grandmother said. "Just remember that the next time you want me to curl your hair."

June Star said her hair was naturally curly.

The next morning the grandmother was the first one in the car, ready to go. She had her big black valise that looked like the head of a hippopotamus in one corner, and underneath it she was hiding a basket with Pitty Sing, the cat, in it. She didn't intend for the cat to be left alone in the house for three days because he would miss her too much and she was afraid he might brush against one of the gas burners and accidentally asphyxiate himself. Her son, Bailey, didn't like to arrive at a motel with a cat.

She sat in the middle of the back seat with John Wesley and June Star on either side of her. Bailey and the children's mother and the baby sat in front and they left Atlanta at eight forty-five with the mileage on the car at 55890. The grandmother wrote this down because she thought it would be interesting to say how many miles they had been when they got back. It took them twenty minutes to reach the outskirts of the city.

The old lady settled herself comfortably, removing her white cotton gloves and putting them up with her purse on the shelf in front of the back window. The children's mother still had on slacks and still had her head tied up in a green kerchief, but the grandmother had on a navy blue straw sailor hat with a bunch of white violets on the brim and a navy blue dress with a small white dot in the print. Her collars and cuffs were white organdy trimmed with lace and at her neckline she had pinned a purple spray of cloth violets containing a sachet. In case of an accident, anyone seeing her dead on the highway would know at once that she was a lady.

She said she thought it was going to be a good day for driving, neither too hot nor too cold, and she cautioned Bailey that the speed limit was fifty-five miles an hour and that the patrolmen hid themselves behind billboards and small clumps of trees and sped out after you before you had a chance to slow down. She pointed out interesting details of the scenery: Stone Mountain; the blue granite that in some places came up to both sides of the highway; the brilliant red clay banks slightly streaked with purple; and the various crops that made rows of green lace-work on the ground. The trees were full of silver-white sunlight and the meanest of them sparkled. The children were reading comic magazines and their mother had gone back to sleep.

"Let's go through Georgia fast so we won't have to look at it much," John Wesley said.

"If I were a little boy," said the grandmother, "I wouldn't talk about my native state that way. Tennessee has the mountains and Georgia has the hills."

"Tennessee is just a hillbilly dumping ground," John Wesley said, "and Georgia is a lousy state too."

"You said it," June Star said.

"In my time," said the grandmother, folding her thin veined fingers, "children were more respectful of their native states and their parents and everything else. People did right then. Oh look at the cute little pickaninny!" she said and pointed to a Negro child standing in the door of a shack. "Wouldn't that make a picture, now?" she asked and they all turned and looked at the little Negro out of the back window. He waved.

"He didn't have any britches on," June Star said.

"He probably didn't have any," the grandmother explained. "Little niggers in the country don't have things like we do. If I could paint, I'd paint that picture," she said.

The children exchanged comic books.

The grandmother offered to hold the baby and the children's mother passed him over the front seat to her. She set him on her knee and bounced him and told him about the things they were passing. She rolled her eyes and screwed up her mouth and stuck her leathery thin face into his smooth bland one. Occasionally he gave her a faraway smile. They passed a large cotton field with five or six graves fenced in the middle of it, like a small island. "Look at the graveyard!" the grandmother said, pointing it out. "That was the old family burying ground. That belonged to the plantation."

"Where's the plantation?" John Wesley asked.

"Gone With the Wind," said the grandmother. "Ha. Ha."

When the children finished all the comic books they had brought, they opened the lunch and ate it. The grandmother ate a peanut butter sandwich and an olive and would not let the children throw the box and the paper napkins out the window. When there was nothing else to do they played a game by choosing a cloud and making the other two guess what shape it suggested. John Wesley took one the shape of a cow and June Star guessed a cow and John Wesley said, no, an automobile, and June Star said he didn't play fair, and they began to slap each other over the grandmother.

The grandmother said she would tell them a story if they would keep quiet. When she told a story, she rolled her eyes and waved her head and was very dramatic. She said once when she was a maiden lady she had been courted by a Mr. Edgar Atkins Teagarden from Jasper, Georgia. She said he was a very good-looking man and a gentleman and that he brought her a watermelon every Saturday afternoon with his initials cut in it. E. A. T. Well, one Saturday, she said, Mr. Teagarden brought the watermelon and there was nobody at home and he left it on the front porch and returned in his buggy to Jasper, but she never got the watermelon, she said, because a nigger boy ate it when he saw the initials, E. A. T.! This story tickled John Wesley's funny bone and he giggled and giggled but June Star didn't think it was any good. She said she wouldn't marry a man that just brought her a watermelon on Saturday. The grandmother said she would have done well to marry Mr. Teagarden because he was a gentleman and had bought Coca-Cola stock when it first came out and that he had died only a few years ago, a very wealthy man.

They stopped at The Tower for barbecued sandwiches. The Tower was a part stucco and part wood filling station and dance hall set in a clearing outside of Timothy. A fat man named Red Sammy Butts ran it and there were signs stuck here and there on the building and for miles up and down the highway saying,

TRY RED SAMMY'S FAMOUS BARBECUE. NONE LIKE FAMOUS RED SAMMY'S! RED SAM! THE FAT BOY WITH THE HAPPY LAUGH. A VETERAN! RED SAMMY'S YOUR MAN!

Red Sammy was lying on the bare ground outside The Tower with his head under a truck while a gray monkey about a foot high, chained to a small chinaberry tree, chattered nearby. The monkey sprang back into the tree and got on the highest limb as soon as he saw the children jump out of the car and run toward him.

Inside, The Tower was a long dark room with a counter at one end and tables at the other and dancing space in the middle. They all sat down at a board table next to the nickelodeon and Red Sam's wife, a tall burnt-brown woman with hair and eyes lighter than her skin, came and took their order. The children's mother put a dime in the machine and played "The Tennessee Waltz," and the grandmother said that tune always made her want to dance. She asked Bailey if he would like to dance but he only glared at her. He didn't have a naturally sunny disposition like she did and trips made him nervous. The grandmother's brown eyes were very bright. She swayed her head from side to side and pretended she was dancing in her chair. June Star said play something she could tap to so the children's mother put in another dime and played a fast number and June Star stepped out onto the dance floor and did her tap routine.

"Ain't she cute?" Red Sam's wife said, leaning over the counter. "Would you like to come be my little girl?"

"No I certainly wouldn't," June Star said. "I wouldn't live in a broken-down place like this for a million bucks!" and she ran back to the table.

"Ain't she cute?" the woman repeated, stretching her mouth politely.

"Aren't you ashamed?" hissed the grandmother.

Red Sam came in and told his wife to quit lounging on the counter and hurry up with these people's order. His khaki trousers reached just to his hip bones and his stomach hung over them like a sack of meal swaying under his shirt. He came over and sat down at a table nearby and let out a combination sigh and yodel. "You can't win," he said. "You can't win," and he wiped his sweating red face off with a gray handkerchief. "These days you don't know who to trust," he said. "Ain't that the truth?"

"People are certainly not nice like they used to be," said the grandmother.

"Two fellers come in here last week," Red Sammy said, "driving a Chrysler. It was a old beat-up car but it was a good one and these boys looked all right to me. Said they worked at the mill and you know I let them fellers charge the gas they bought? Now why did I do that?"

"Because you're a good man!" the grandmother said at once.

"Yes'm, I suppose so," Red Sam said as if he were struck with this answer.

His wife brought the orders, carrying the five plates all at once without a tray, two in each hand and one balanced on her arm. "It isn't a soul in this green world of God's that you can trust," she said. "And I don't count nobody out of that, not nobody," she repeated, looking at Red Sammy.

199

"Did you read about that criminal, The Misfit, that's escaped?" asked the grandmother.

"I wouldn't be a bit surprised if he didn't attack this place right here," said the woman. "If he hears about it being here, I wouldn't be none surprised to see him. If he hears it's two cent in the cash register, I wouldn't be at all surprised if he . . ."

"That'll do," Red Sam said. "Go bring these people their Co-'Colas," and the woman went off to get the rest of the order.

"A good man is hard to find," Red Sammy said. "Everything is getting terrible. I remember the day you could go off and leave your screen door unlatched. Not no more."

200   He and the grandmother discussed better times. The old lady said that in her opinion Europe was entirely to blame for the way things were now. She said the way Europe acted you would think we were made of money and Red Sam said it was no use talking about it, she was exactly right. The children ran outside into the white sunlight and looked at the monkey in the lacy chinaberry tree. He was busy catching fleas on himself and biting each one carefully between his teeth as if it were a delicacy.

They drove off again into the hot afternoon. The grandmother took cat naps and woke up every few minutes with her own snoring. Outside of Toombsboro she woke up and recalled an old plantation that she had visited in this neighborhood once when she was a young lady. She said the house had six white columns across the front and that there was an avenue of oaks leading up to it and two little wooden trellis arbors on either side in front where you sat down with your suitor after a stroll in the garden. She recalled exactly which road to turn off to get to it. She knew that Bailey would not be willing to lose any time looking at an old house, but the more she talked about it, the more she wanted to see it once again and find out if the little twin arbors were still standing. "There was a secret panel in this house," she said craftily, not telling the truth but wishing that she were, "and the story went that all the family silver was hidden in it when Sherman came through but it was never found . . ."

"Hey!" John Wesley said. "Let's go see it! We'll find it! We'll poke all the woodwork and find it! Who lives there? Where do you turn off at? Hey Pop, can't we turn off there?"

"We never have seen a house with a secret panel!" June Star shrieked. "Let's go to the house with the secret panel! Hey Pop, can't we go see the house with the secret panel!"

"It's not far from here, I know," the grandmother said. "It wouldn't take over twenty minutes."

Bailey was looking straight ahead. His jaw was as rigid as a horseshoe. "No," he said.

The children began to yell and scream that they wanted to see the house with the secret panel. John Wesley kicked the back of the front seat and June Star hung over her mother's shoulder and whined desperately into her ear that they never had any fun even on their vacation, that they could never do what THEY wanted to do. The baby began to scream and John Wesley kicked the back of the seat so hard that his father could feel the blows in his kidney.

"All right!" he shouted and drew the car to a stop at the side of the road. "Will you all shut up? Will you all just shut up for one second? If you don't shut up, we won't go anywhere."

"It would be very educational for them," the grandmother murmured.

"All right," Bailey said, "but get this: this is the only time we're going to stop for anything like this. This is the one and only time."

"The dirt road that you have to turn down is about a mile back," the grandmother directed. "I marked it when we passed."

"A dirt road," Bailey groaned.

After they had turned around and were headed toward the dirt road, the grand- mother recalled other points about the house, the beautiful glass over the front doorway and the candle-lamp in the hall. John Wesley said that the secret panel was probably in the fireplace.

"You can't go inside this house," Bailey said. "You don't know who lives there."

"While you all talk to the people in front, I'll run around behind and get in a window," John Wesley suggested.

"We'll all stay in the car," his mother said.

They turned onto the dirt road and the car raced roughly along in a swirl of pink dust. The grandmother recalled the times when there were no paved roads and thirty miles was a day's journey. The dirt road was hilly and there were sudden washes in it and sharp curves on dangerous embankments. All at once they would be on a hill, looking down over the blue tops of trees for miles around, then the next minute, they would be in a red depression with the dust-coated trees looking down on them.

"This place had better turn up in a minute," Bailey said, "or I'm going to turn around."

The road looked as if no one had traveled on it in months.

"It's not much farther," the grandmother said and just as she said it, a horrible thought came to her. The thought was so embarrassing that she turned red in the face and her eyes dilated and her feet jumped up, upsetting her valise in the corner. The instant the valise moved, the newspaper top she had over the basket under it rose with a snarl and Pitty Sing, the cat, sprang onto Bailey's shoulder.

The children were thrown to the floor and their mother, clutching the baby, was thrown out the door onto the ground; the old lady was thrown into the front seat. The car turned over once and landed right-side-up in a gulch off the side of the road. Bailey remained in the driver's seat with the cat—gray-striped with a broad white face and an orange nose—clinging to his neck like a caterpillar.

As soon as the children saw they could move their arms and legs, they scrambled out of the car, shouting, "We've had an ACCIDENT!" The grandmother was curled up under the dashboard, hoping she was injured so that Bailey's wrath would not come down on her all at once. The horrible thought she had had before the accident was that the house she had remembered so vividly was not in Georgia but in Tennessee.

Bailey removed the cat from his neck with both hands and flung it out the window against the side of a pine tree. Then he got out of the car and started looking for the children's mother. She was sitting against the side of the red gutted ditch, holding the screaming baby, but she only had a cut down her face and a broken shoulder. "We've had an ACCIDENT!" the children screamed in a frenzy of delight.

"But nobody's killed," June Star said with disappointment as the grandmother limped out of the car, her hat still pinned to her head but the broken front brim standing up at a jaunty angle and the violet spray hanging off the side. They all sat down in the ditch, except the children, to recover from the shock. They were all shaking.

"Maybe a car will come along," said the children's mother hoarsely.

"I believe I have an injured organ," said the grandmother, pressing her side, but no one answered her. Bailey's teeth were clattering. He had on a yellow sport shirt with bright blue parrots designed on it and his face was as yellow as the shirt. The grandmother decided that she would not mention that the house was in Tennessee.

The road was about ten feet above and they could see only the tops of the trees on the other side of it. Behind the ditch they were sitting in there were more woods, tall and dark and deep. In a few minutes they saw a car some distance away on top of a hill, coming slowly as if the occupants were watching them. The grandmother stood up and waved both arms dramatically to attract their attention. The car continued to come on slowly, disappeared around a bend and appeared again, moving even slower, on top of the hill they had gone over. It was a big black battered hearse-like automobile. There were three men in it.

It came to a stop just over them and for some minutes, the driver looked down with a steady expressionless gaze to where they were sitting, and didn't speak. Then he turned his head and muttered something to the other two and they got out. One was a fat boy in black trousers and a red sweat shirt with a silver stallion embossed on the front of it. He moved around on the right side of them and stood staring, his mouth partly open in a kind of loose grin. The other had on khaki pants and a blue striped coat and a gray hat pulled down very low, hiding most of his face. He came around slowly on the left side. Neither spoke.

The driver got out of the car and stood by the side of it, looking down at them. He was an older man than the other two. His hair was just beginning to gray and he wore silver-rimmed spectacles that give him a scholarly look. He had a long creased face and didn't have on any shirt or undershirt. He had on blue jeans that were too tight for him and was holding a black hat and a gun. The two boys also had guns.

"We've had an ACCIDENT!" the children screamed.

The grandmother had the peculiar feeling that the bespectacled man was someone she knew. His face was as familiar to her as if she had known him all her life but she could not recall who he was. He moved away from the car and began to come down the embankment, placing his feet carefully so that he wouldn't slip. He had on tan and white shoes and no socks, and his ankles were red and thin. "Good afternoon," he said. "I see you all had you a little spill."

"We turned over twice!" said the grandmother.

"Oncet," he corrected. "We seen it happen. Try their car and see will it run, Hiram," he said quietly to the boy with the gray hat.

"What you got that gun for?" John Wesley asked. "Whatcha gonna do with that gun?"

"Lady," the man said to the children's mother, "would you mind calling them children to sit down by you? Children make me nervous. I want all you to sit down right together there where you're at."

"What are you telling US what to do for?" June Star asked.

Behind them the line of woods gaped like a dark open mouth. "Come here," said their mother.

"Look here now," Bailey began suddenly, "we're in a predicament! We're in . . ."

The grandmother shrieked. She scrambled to her feet and stood staring. "You're The Misfit!" she said. "I recognized you at once!"

"Yes'm," the man said, smiling slightly as if he were pleased in spite of himself to be known, "but it would have been better for all of you, lady, if you hadn't reckernized me."

Bailey turned his head sharply and said something to his mother that shocked even the children. The old lady began to cry and The Misfit reddened.

"Lady," he said, "don't you get upset. Sometimes a man says things he don't mean. I don't reckon he meant to talk to you thataway."

"You wouldn't shoot a lady, would you?" the grandmother said and removed the clean handkerchief from her cuff and began to slap at her eyes with it.

The Misfit pointed the toe of his shoe into the ground and made a little hole and then covered it up again. "I would hate to have to," he said.

"Listen," the grandmother almost screamed, "I know you're a good man. You don't look a bit like you have common blood. I know you must come from nice people!"

"Yes mam," he said, "finest people in the world." When he smiled he showed a row of strong white teeth. "God never made a finer woman than my mother and my daddy's heart was pure gold," he said. The boy with the red sweat shirt had come around behind them and was standing with his gun at his hip. The Misfit squatted down on the ground. "Watch them children, Bobby Lee," he said. "You know they make me nervous." He looked at the six of them huddled together in front of him and he seemed to be embarrassed as if he couldn't think of anything to say. "Ain't a cloud in the sky," he remarked, looking up at it. "Don't see no sun but don't see no cloud neither."

"Yes, it's a beautiful day," said the grandmother. "Listen," she said, "you shouldn't call yourself The Misfit because I know you're a good man at heart. I can just look at you and tell."

"Hush!" Bailey yelled. "Hush! Everybody shut up and let me handle this!" He was squatting in the position of a runner about to sprint forward but he didn't move.

"I pre-chate that, lady," The Misfit said and drew a little circle in the ground with the butt of his gun.

"It'll take a half a hour to fix this here car," Hiram called, looking over the raised hood of it.

"Well, first you and Bobby Lee get him and that little boy to step over yonder with you," The Misfit said, pointing to Bailey and John Wesley. "The boys want to ask you something," he said to Bailey. "Would you mind stepping back in them woods there with them?"

"Listen," Bailey began, "we're in a terrible predicament! Nobody realizes what this is," and his voice cracked. His eyes were as blue and intense as the parrots on his shirt and he remained perfectly still.

The grandmother reached up to adjust her hat brim as if she were going to the woods with him but it came off in her hand. She stood staring at it and after a second she let it fall on the ground. Hiram pulled Bailey up by the arm as if he were assisting an old man. John Wesley caught hold of his father's hand and Bobby Lee followed. They went off toward the woods and just as they reached the dark edge, Bailey turned and supported himself against a gray naked pine trunk; he shouted, "I'll be back in a minute, Mamma, wait on me!"

"Come back this instant!" his mother shrilled but they all disappeared into the woods.

"Bailey Boy!" the grandmother called in a tragic voice but she found she was looking at The Misfit squatting on the ground in front of her. "I just know you're a good man," she said desperately. "You're not a bit common!"

"Nome, I ain't a good man," The Misfit said after a second as if he had considered her statement carefully, "but I ain't the worst in the world neither. My daddy said I was a different breed of dog from my brothers and sisters. 'You know,' Daddy said, 'it's some that can live their whole life out without asking about it and it's others has to know why it is, and this boy is one of the latters. He's going to be into everything!'" He put on his black hat and looked up suddenly and then away deep into the woods as if he were embarrassed again. "I'm sorry I don't have on a shirt before you ladies," he said, hunching his shoulders slightly. "We buried our clothes that we had on when we escaped and we're just making do until we can get better. We borrowed these from some folks we met," he explained.

"That's perfectly all right," the grandmother said. "Maybe Bailey has an extra shirt in his suitcase."

"I'll look and see terrectly," The Misfit said.

"Where are they taking him?" the children's mother screamed.

"Daddy was a card himself," The Misfit said. "You couldn't put anything over on him. He never got in trouble with the Authorities though. Just had the knack of handling them."

"You could be honest too if you'd only try," said the grandmother. "Think how wonderful it would be to settle down and live a comfortable life and not have to think about somebody chasing you all the time."

The Misfit kept scratching in the ground with the butt of his gun as if he were thinking about it. "Yes'm, somebody is always after you," he murmured.

The grandmother noticed how thin his shoulder blades were just behind his hat because she was standing up looking down on him. "Do you ever pray?" she asked.

He shook his head. All she saw was the black hat wiggle between his shoulder blades. "Nome," he said.

There was a pistol shot from the woods, followed closely by another. Then silence. The old lady's head jerked around. She could hear the wind move through the tree tops like a long satisfied insuck of breath. "Bailey Boy!" she called.

"I was a gospel singer for a while," The Misfit said. "I been most everything. Been in the arm service, both land and sea, at home and abroad, been twict married, been an undertaker, been with the railroads, plowed Mother Earth, been in a tornado, seen a man burnt alive oncet," and he looked up at the children's mother and the little girl who were sitting close together, their faces white and their eyes glassy; "I even seen a woman flogged," he said.

"Pray, pray," the grandmother began, "pray, pray . . ."

"I never was a bad boy that I remember of," The Misfit said in an almost dreamy voice, "but somewheres along the line I done something wrong and got sent to the penitentiary. I was buried alive," and he looked up and held her attention to him by a steady stare.

"That's when you should have started to pray," she said. "What did you do to get sent to the penitentiary that first time?"

"Turn to the right, it was a wall," The Misfit said, looking up again at the cloudless sky. "Turn to the left, it was a wall. Look up it was a ceiling, look down it was a floor. I forget what I done, lady. I set there and set there, trying to remember what it was I done and I ain't recalled it to this day. Oncet in a while, I would think it was coming to me, but it never come."

"Maybe they put you in by mistake," the old lady said vaguely.

"Nome," he said. "It wasn't no mistake. They had the papers on me."

"You must have stolen something," she said.

The Misfit sneered slightly. "Nobody had nothing I wanted," he said. "It was a head-doctor at the penitentiary said what I had done was kill my daddy but I known that for a lie. My daddy died in nineteen ought nineteen of the epidemic flu and I never had a thing to do with it. He was buried in the Mount Hopewell Baptist churchyard and you can go there and see for yourself."

"If you would pray," the old lady said, "Jesus would help you."

"That's right," The Misfit said.

"Well then, why don't you pray?" she asked trembling with delight suddenly.

"I don't want no hep," he said. "I'm doing all right by myself."

Bobby Lee and Hiram came ambling back from the woods. Bobby Lee was dragging a yellow shirt with bright blue parrots in it.

"Throw me that shirt, Bobby Lee," The Misfit said. The shirt came flying at him and landed on his shoulder and he put it on. The grandmother couldn't name what the shirt reminded her of. "No, lady," The Misfit said while he was buttoning it up, "I found out the crime don't matter. You can do one thing or you can do another, kill a man or take a tire off his car, because sooner or later you're going to forget what it was you done and just be punished for it."

The children's mother had begun to make heaving noises as if she couldn't get her breath. "Lady," he asked, "would you and that little girl like to step off yonder with Bobby Lee and Hiram and join your husband?"

"Yes, thank you," the mother said faintly. Her left arm dangled helplessly and she was holding the baby, who had gone to sleep, in the other. "Hep that lady up, Hiram," The Misfit said as she struggled to climb out of the ditch, "and Bobby Lee, you hold onto that little girl's hand."

"I don't want to hold hands with him," June Star said. "He reminds me of a pig."

The fat boy blushed and laughed and caught her by the arm and pulled her off into the woods after Hiram and her mother.

Alone with The Misfit, the grandmother found that she had lost her voice. There was not a cloud in the sky nor any sun. There was nothing around her but woods. She wanted to tell him that he must pray. She opened and closed her mouth several times before anything came out. Finally she found herself saying, "Jesus, Jesus," meaning, Jesus will help you, but the way she was saying it, it sounded as if she might be cursing.

"Yes'm," The Misfit said as if he agreed. "Jesus thown everything off balance. It was the same case with Him as with me except He hadn't committed any crime and they could prove I had committed one because they had the papers on me. Of course," he said, "they never shown me my papers. That's why I sign myself now. I said long ago, you get you a signature and sign everything you do and keep a copy of it. Then you'll know what you done and you can hold up the crime to the punishment and see do they match and in the end you'll have something to prove you ain't been treated right. I call myself The Misfit," he said, "because I can't make what all I done wrong fit what all I gone through in punishment."

There was a piercing scream from the woods, followed closely by a pistol report. "Does it seem right to you, lady, that one is punished a heap and another ain't punished at all?"

"Jesus!" the old lady cried. "You've got good blood! I know you wouldn't shoot a lady! I know you come from nice people! Pray! Jesus, you ought not to shoot a lady. I'll give you all the money I've got!"

"Lady," The Misfit said, looking beyond her far into the woods, "there never was a body that give the undertaker a tip."

There were two more pistol reports and the grandmother raised her head like a parched old turkey hen crying for water and called, "Bailey Boy, Bailey Boy!" as if her heart would break.

"Jesus was the only One that ever raised the dead," The Misfit continued, "and He shouldn't have done it. He thown everything off balance. If He did what He said, then it's nothing for you to do but thow away everything and follow Him, and if He didn't, then it's nothing for you to do but enjoy the few minutes you got left the best way you can—by killing somebody or burning down his house or doing some other meanness to him. No pleasure but meanness," he said and his voice had become almost a snarl.

"Maybe He didn't raise the dead," the old lady mumbled, not knowing what she was saying and feeling so dizzy that she sank down in the ditch with her legs twisted under her.

"I wasn't there so I can't say He didn't," The Misfit said. "I wisht I had of been there," he said, hitting the ground with his fist. "It ain't right I wasn't there because if I had of been there I would of known. Listen lady," he said in a high voice, "if I had of been there I would have known and I wouldn't be like I am now." His voice seemed about to crack and the grandmother's head cleared for an instant. She saw the man's face twisted close to her own as if he were going to cry and she murmured, "Why you're one of my babies. You're one of my own children!" She reached out and touched him on the shoulder. The Misfit sprang back as if a snake had bitten him and shot her three times through the chest. Then he put his gun down on the ground and took off his glasses and began to clean them.

Hiram and Bobby Lee returned from the woods and stood over the ditch, looking down at the grandmother who half sat and half lay in a puddle of blood with her legs crossed under her like a child's and her face smiling up at the cloudless sky.

Without his glasses, The Misfit's eyes were red-rimmed and pale and defenseless-looking. "Take her off and thow her where you thown the others," he said, picking up the cat that was rubbing itself against his leg.

"She was a talker, wasn't she?" Bobby Lee said, sliding down the ditch with a yodel.

"She would of been a good woman," The Misfit said, "if it had been somebody there to shoot her every minute of her life."

"Some fun!" Bobby Lee said.

"Shut up, Bobby Lee," The Misfit said. "It's no real pleasure in life."

208   I think it is the year 1909. I feel as if I were in a motion picture theatre, the long arm of light crossing the darkness and spinning, my eyes fixed on the screen. This is a silent picture as if an old Biograph one, in which the actors are dressed in ridiculously old-fashioned clothes, and one flash succeeds another with sudden jumps. The actors too seem to jump about and walk too fast. The shots themselves are full of dots and rays, as if it were raining when the picture was photographed. The light is bad.

   It is Sunday afternoon, June 12, 1909, and my father is walking down the quiet streets of Brooklyn on his way to visit my mother. His clothes are newly pressed and his tie is too tight in his high collar. He jingles the coins in his pockets, thinking of the witty things he will say. I feel as if I had by now relaxed entirely in the soft darkness of the theatre; the organist peals out the obvious and approximate emotions on which the audience rocks unknowingly. I am anonymous, and I have forgotten myself. It is always so when one goes to the movies, it is, as they say, a drug.

   My father walks from street to street of trees, lawns and houses, once in a while coming to an avenue on which a street-car skates and gnaws, slowly progressing. The conductor, who has a handle-bar mustache, helps a young lady wearing a hat like a bowl with feathers on to the car. She lifts her long skirts slightly as she mounts the steps. He leisurely makes change and rings his bell. It is obviously Sunday, for everyone is wearing Sunday clothes, and the street-car's noises emphasize the quiet of the holiday. Is not Brooklyn the city of Churches? The shops are closed and their shades drawn, but for an occasional stationery store or drugstore with great green balls in the window.

   My father has chosen to take this long walk because he likes to walk and think. He thinks about himself in the future and so arrives at the place he is to visit in a state of mild exaltation. He pays no attention to the houses he is passing, in which the Sunday dinner is being eaten, nor to the many trees which patrol each street, now coming to their full leafage and the time when they will room

---

the whole street in cool shadow. An occasional carriage passes, the horse's hooves falling like stones in the quiet afternoon, and once in a while an automobile, looking like an enormous upholstered sofa, puffs and passes.

My father thinks of my mother, of how nice it will be to introduce her to his family. But he is not yet sure that he wants to marry her, and once in a while he becomes panicky about the bond already established. He reassures himself by thinking of the big men he admires who are married: William Randolph Hearst, and William Howard Taft, who has just become President of the United States.

My father arrives at my mother's house. He has come too early and so is suddenly embarrassed. My aunt, my mother's sister, answers the loud bell with her napkin in her hand, for the family is still at dinner. As my father enters, my grandfather rises from the table and shakes hands with him. My mother has run upstairs to tidy herself. My grandmother asks my father if he has had dinner, and tells him that Rose will be downstairs soon. My grandfather opens the conversation by remarking on the mild June weather. My father sits uncomfortably near the table, holding his hat in his hand. My grandmother tells my aunt to take my father's hat. My uncle, twelve years old, runs into the house, his hair tousled. He shouts a greeting to my father, who has often given him a nickel, and then runs upstairs. It is evident that the respect in which my father is held in this household is tempered by a good deal of mirth. He is impressive, yet he is very awkward.

209

Finally my mother comes downstairs, all dressed up, and my father being engaged in conversation with my grandfather becomes uneasy, not knowing whether to greet my mother or continue the conversation. He gets up from the chair clumsily and says "hello" gruffly. My grandfather watches, examining their congruence, such as it is, with a critical eye, and meanwhile rubbing his bearded cheek roughly, as he always does when he reflects. He is worried; he is afraid that my father will not make a good husband for his oldest daughter. At this point something happens to the film, just as my father is saying something funny to my mother; I am awakened to myself and my unhappiness just as my interest was rising. The audience begins to clap impatiently. Then the trouble is cared for but the film has been returned to a portion just shown, and once more I see my grandfather rubbing his bearded cheek and pondering my father's character. It is difficult to get back into the picture once more and forget myself, but as my mother giggles at my father's words, the darkness drowns me.

My father and mother depart from the house, my father shaking hands with my mother once more, out of some unknown uneasiness. I stir uneasily also, slouched in the hard chair of the theatre. Where is the older uncle, my mother's older brother? He is studying in his bedroom upstairs, studying for his final examination at the College of the City of New York, having been dead of rapid pneumonia for the last twenty-one years. My mother and father walk down the same quiet streets once more. My mother is holding my father's arm and telling him of the novel which she has been reading; and my father utters judgments of the characters as the plot is made clear to him. This is a habit which he very much enjoys, for he feels the utmost superiority and confidence when he approves and condemns the behavior of other people. At times he feels moved to utter a brief "Ugh,"—whenever the story becomes what he would call sugary. This tribute is paid to his manliness. My mother feels satisfied by the interest which she has awakened; she is showing my father how intelligent she is, and how interesting.

They reach the avenue, and the street-car leisurely arrives. They are going to Coney Island this afternoon, although my mother considers that such pleasures are inferior. She has made up her mind to indulge only in a walk on the boardwalk and a pleasant dinner, avoiding the riotous amusements as being beneath the dignity of so dignified a couple.

My father tells my mother how much money he has made in the past week, exaggerating an amount which need not have been exaggerated. But my father has always felt that actualities somehow fall short. Suddenly I begin to weep. The determined old lady who sits next to me in the theatre is annoyed and looks at me with an angry face, and being intimidated, I stop. I drag out my handkerchief and dry my face, licking the drop which has fallen near my lips. Meanwhile I have missed something, for here are my mother and father alighting at the last stop, Coney Island.

They walk toward the boardwalk, and my father commands my mother to inhale the pungent air from the sea. They both breathe in deeply, both of them laughing as they do so. They have in common a great interest in health, although my father is strong and husky, my mother frail. Their minds are full of theories of what is good to eat and not good to eat, and sometimes they engage in heated discussions of the subject, the whole matter ending in my father's announcement, made with a scornful bluster, that you have to die sooner or later anyway. On the boardwalk's flagpole, the American flag is pulsing in an intermittent wind from the sea.

My father and mother go to the rail of the boardwalk and look down on the beach where a good many bathers are casually walking about. A few are in the surf. A peanut whistle pierces the air with its pleasant and active whine, and my father goes to buy peanuts. My mother remains at the rail and stares at the ocean. The ocean seems merry to her; it pointedly sparkles and again and again the pony waves are released. She notices the children digging in the wet sand, and the bathing costumes of the girls who are her own age. My father returns with the peanuts. Overhead the sun's lightning strikes and strikes, but neither of them are at all aware of it. The boardwalk is full of people dressed in their Sunday clothes and idly strolling. The tide does not reach as far as the boardwalk, and the strollers would feel no danger if it did. My mother and father lean on the rail of the boardwalk and absently stare at the ocean. The ocean is becoming rough; the waves come in slowly, tugging strength from far back. The moment before they somersault, the moment when they arch their backs so beautifully, showing green and white veins amid the black, that moment is intolerable. They finally crack, dashing fiercely upon the sand, actually driving, full force downward, against the sand, bouncing upward and forward, and at last petering out into a small stream which races up the beach and then is recalled. My parents gaze absentmindedly at the ocean, scarcely interested in its harshness. The sun overhead does not disturb them. But I stare at the terrible sun which breaks up sight, and the fatal, merciless, passionate ocean, I forget my parents. I stare fascinated and finally, shocked by the indifference of my father and mother, I burst out weeping once more. The old lady next to me pats me on the shoulder and says "There, there, all of this is only a movie, young man, only a movie," but I look up once more at the terrifying sun and the terrifying ocean, and being unable to control my tears, I get up and go to the men's room, stumbling over the feet of the other people seated in my row.

When I return, feeling as if I had awakened in the morning sick for lack of sleep, several hours have apparently passed and my parents are riding on the merry-go-round. My father is on a black horse, and my mother on a white one, and they seem to be making an eternal circuit for the single purpose of snatching the nickel rings which are attached to the arm of one of the posts. A hand-organ is playing; it is one with the ceaseless circling of the merry-go-round.

211

For a moment it seems that they will never get off the merry-go-round because it will never stop. I feel like one who looks down on the avenue from the 50th story of a building. But at length they do get off; even the music of the hand-organ has ceased for a moment. My father has acquired ten rings, my mother only two, although it was my mother who really wanted them.

They walk on along the boardwalk as the afternoon descends by imperceptible degrees into the incredible violet of dusk. Everything fades into a relaxed glow, even the ceaseless murmuring from the beach, and the revolutions of the merry-go-round. They look for a place to have dinner. My father suggests the best one on the boardwalk and my mother demurs, in accordance with her principles.

However they do go to the best place, asking for a table near the window, so that they can look out on the boardwalk and the mobile ocean. My father feels omnipotent as he places a quarter in the waiter's hand as he asks for a table. The place is crowded and here too there is music, this time from a kind of string trio. My father orders dinner with a fine confidence.

As the dinner is eaten, my father tells of his plans for the future, and my mother shows with expressive face how interested she is, and how impressed. My father becomes exultant. He is lifted up by the waltz that is being played, and his own future begins to intoxicate him. My father tells my mother that he is going to expand his business, for there is a great deal of money to be made. He wants to settle down. After all, he is twenty-nine, he has lived by himself since he was thirteen, he is making more and more money, and he is envious of his married friends when he visits them in the cozy security of their homes, surrounded, it seems, by the calm domestic pleasures, and by delightful children, and then, as the waltz reaches the moment when all the dancers swing madly, then, then with awful daring, then he asks my mother to marry him, although awkwardly enough and puzzled, even in his excitement, at how he had arrived at the proposal, and she, to make the whole business worse, begins to cry, and my father looks nervously about, not knowing at all what to do now, and my mother says: "It's all I've wanted from the moment I saw you," sobbing, and he finds all of this very difficult, scarcely to his taste, scarcely as he had thought it would be, on his long walks over Brooklyn Bridge in the revery of a fine cigar, and it was then that I stood up in the theatre and shouted: "Don't do it. It's not too late to change your minds, both of you. Nothing good will come of it, only remorse, hatred, scandal, and two children whose characters are monstrous." The whole audience turned to look at me, annoyed, the usher came hurrying down the aisle flashing his search-light, and the old lady next to me tugged me down into my seat, saying: "Be quiet. You'll be put out, and you paid thirty-five cents to come in." And so I shut my eyes because I could not bear to see what was happening. I sat there quietly.

212

But after awhile I begin to take brief glimpses, and at length I watch again with thirsty interest, like a child who wants to maintain his sulk although offered the bribe of candy. My parents are now having their picture taken in a photographer's booth along the boardwalk. The place is shadowed in the mauve light which is apparently necessary. The camera is set to the side on its tripod and looks like a Martian man. The photographer is instructing my parents in how to pose. My father has his arm over my mother's shoulder, and both of them smile emphatic-ally. The photographer brings my mother a bouquet of flowers to hold in her hand but she holds it at the wrong angle. Then the photographer covers himself with the black cloth which drapes the camera and all that one sees of him is one protruding arm and his hand which clutches the rubber ball which he will squeeze when the picture is finally taken. But he is not satisfied with their appearance. He feels with certainty that somehow there is something wrong in their pose. Again and again he issues from his hidden place with new directions. Each suggestion merely makes matters worse. My father is becoming impatient. They try a seated pose. The photographer explains that he has pride, he is not interested in all of this for the money, he wants to make beautiful pictures. My father says: "Hurry up, will you? We haven't got all night." But the photographer only scurries about apologetically, and issues new directions. The photographer charms me. I approve of him with all my heart, for I know just how he feels, and as he criticizes each revised pose according to some unknown idea of rightness. I become quite hopeful. But then my father says angrily: "Come on, you've had enough time, we're not going to wait any longer." And the photographer, sighing unhappily, goes back under his black covering, holds out his hands, says: "One, two, three, Now!", and the picture is taken, with my father's smile turned to a grimace and my mother's bright and false. It takes a few minutes for the picture to be developed and as my parents sit in the curious light they become quite depressed.

They have passed a fortune-teller's booth, and my mother wishes to go in, but my father does not. They begin to argue about it. My mother becomes stubborn, my father once more impatient, and then they begin to quarrel, and what my father would like to do is walk off and leave my mother there, but he knows that that would never do. My mother refuses to budge. She is near to tears, but she feels an uncontrollable desire to hear what the palm-reader will say. My father consents angrily, and they both go into a booth which is in a way like the photographer's, since it is draped in black cloth and its light is shadowed. The place is too warm, and my father keeps saying this is all nonsense, pointing to the crystal ball on the table. The fortune-teller, a fat, short woman, garbed in what is supposed to be Oriental robes, comes into the room from the back and greets them, speaking with an accent. But suddenly my father feels that the whole thing is intolerable; he tugs at my mother's arm, but my mother refuses to budge. And then, in terrible anger, my father lets go of my mother's arm and strides out, leaving my mother stunned. She moves to go after my father, but the fortune-teller holds her arm tightly and begs her not to do so, and I in my seat am shocked more than can ever be said, for I feel as if I were walking a tight-rope a hundred feet over a circus-audience and suddenly the rope is showing signs of breaking, and I get up from my seat and begin to shout once more the first words I can think of to communicate my terrible fear and once more the usher comes hurrying down the aisle flashing his searchlight, and the old lady pleads with me, and the shocked audience has turned to stare at me, and I keep shouting: "What are they doing? Don't they know what they are doing? Why doesn't my mother go after my father? If she does not do that, what will she do? Doesn't my father know what he is doing?"—But the usher has seized my arm and is dragging me away, and as he does so, he says: "What are *you* doing? Don't you know that you can't do whatever you want to do? Why should a young man like you, with your whole life before you, get hysterical like this? Why don't you *think* of what you're doing? You can't act like this even if other people aren't around! You will be sorry if you do not do what you should do, you can't carry on like this, it is not right, you will find that out soon enough, everything you do matters too much," and he said that dragging me through the lobby of the theatre into the cold light, and I woke up into the bleak winter morning of my 21st birthday, the windowsill shining with its lip of snow, and the morning already begun.

213